TAG, I'M IT!

A Daily Journal of Thanks-Giving, Act-Knowledge-ment, and Gratitude

Maureen Ryan Griffin

FLOATING LEAF PRESS

ACKNOWLEDGMENTS

Much gratitude to Bridgett Bell Langson, Wendy H. Gill, and Kim Love Stump for their creative insights and support in making this book better than it would have been. Special thanks to my entire class of Under Construction writers who served as a pilot group and provided valuable feedback: Amy Cole, Bridgett Bell Langson, Cindy Campbell, Cheryl Boyer, Jennifer Hurlbert, Kathy Brown, Kathy Gruhn, Kim Love Stump, Lisa Kunkleman, Mary Struble Deery, Rachelle McClintock, and T.D. Taegel, I know it is a cliché, but you truly do light up my life each week with your talent, heart, and generosity. I am ever grateful to my family and friends, especially my husband, Richard, whose love and steadiness is such ballast when my flights of fancy lift me too high aloft.

Thanks to Vecteezy.com for the use of the graphic
that accompanies the daily quotes.

Author photograph by Donna Foster Photography
at www.donnafoster.com.

Published in the United States of America by

FLOATING LEAF PRESS

A division of

WordPlay

Maureen Ryan Griffin
6420 A-1 Rea Road, Suite 218, Charlotte, NC 28277
Email: info@wordplaynow.com
www.wordplaynow.com

ISBN 978-0-9802304-7-5

For Bridgett,
whose faith in me
and enthusiasm for this practice
gave me the courage and fortitude I needed
to bring this book into being

Welcome to the *TAG, I'M IT!* Journal

This simple practice offers, in only five to fifteen minutes a day, a powerful way to experience a substantively greater sense of contentment and fulfillment. I hope you'll come to love taking a few quiet moments in the evening to reflect on the good in your life. The process of writing out three* "T"s (things you're thankful for), "A"s (actions you can acknowledge yourself for), and "G"s (gifts of the day you're grateful for) is a transformative one, especially combined with the final step, "I'M IT!," in which you intentionally choose three do-able, most-important-to-you actions you'll take the next day. Over time, you'll find you're living your days with more joy, presence, purpose, and intention.

*more are fine, but not needed

Why *three* "T's," "A's," "G's" and "I'M IT's"?

Because three are enough, over time, to cause profound change. And, even on the fullest days, three is a do-able number. (Plus, three is lucky; after all, it's the number of wishes fairies grant in fairy tales.)

Why the evening?

Because the *TAG, I'M IT!* practice is an uplifting way to end your day and promote peaceful rest, allowing you to settle your thoughts and emotions, appreciate the goodness in your life, and dwell on what matters most to you rather than what may have saddened, disappointed, angered, or upset you.

Because you'll soon begin to, all day long, think about what you'll write in your *TAG, I'M IT!* journal. You'll find yourself noticing blessings large and small; gifts of kindness, empathy, time, talent, and treasure; synchronicities and serendipities that make you smile. (Linda Matney, a dear friend of mine who is a spiritual powerhouse, calls these "God-incidences.") Becoming present to these experiences is good for you—in mind, body, heart, and spirit.

Full disclosure: Sometimes I'm so tired by the time my evening winds to a close that I save my *TAG, I'M IT!* for the following morning. It gets my day started off well, and still makes a big difference. And I don't, in real life, do this practice every single day. Doing it most, or many, or even some days is OK. Take this flexibility to heart. This journal is an invitation, not another to-do on your list.

An idea I love: I've taken to carrying my *TAG, I'M IT!* journal around with me so that, whenever I feel thankful for something or someone; accomplish something I feel good about; or receive a gift—tangible or intangible—I can write it down right then. Not only am I guaranteeing that my loveliest moments won't be buried forever in the avalanche of tasks, interruptions, and distractions of my day, I'm also delighted when evening comes and my journal already has entries in it. The word *savor* comes to mind when I recall how this feels to me. Try this if it sounds good to you.

Here are some thoughts and suggestions so you'll get the most out of each part of the process:

THE DATE

While you, of course, know how to fill in a date, this is a good place to tell you that this space is blank for TWO reasons: so you can start any day you like, and because you may possibly fail to fill in your Thanksgiving, Acknowledgment, Gratitude, and I'm It! sections every single day. (If the word *fail* evoked discomfort or anxiety, or if you felt fear ricochet through your body, take a deep breath! Be assured that this journey isn't about perfection or proving anything about yourself. It's about leaning into thanksgiving, acknowledgment, gratitude, and intention, learning and growing all the while.) If you skip a day, or even a number of days, Your *TAG, I'M IT!* journal is waiting, without judgment, for you to resume recording the details and delights that comprise the ultimate gift—your life.

THE BLANK SPACE TO THE RIGHT OF THE DATE

One of the women who tested *TAG, I'M IT!* noted that it provides an invaluable record of the best moments of one's days—a bonus benefit, one that's especially meaningful on noteworthy days, like a birthday or New Year's Day. Another reader suggested I add a place for a daily highlight. I loved the idea—this could be something included in one of the "T," "A," or "G" lists, or a different entry altogether. Thinking about highlights reminded me of a poem by Joyce Sutphen called "The Book of Hours" in which she recounts beautiful hours in her life: like the hour, back in the 70s, sitting on a blanket in Central Park as Pete Seeger sang, "This Land Is Your Land," and the hour drinking in art at the Tate Britain museum in London, and the hour in which she rescued a runaway dog from a busy road. Sutphen ends with the words, "that was an hour well/spent. Yes, that was a keeper."

What from your day will you choose as "a keeper"? When you leaf back through your *TAG, I'M IT!* journal, there it'll be, preserved for you to enjoy again.

The first printing of this book had the word "HIGHLIGHT" written in the upper left corner of this space on the top right of the page. Then, several people who were using, and loving, their *TAG, I'M IT!* journal expressed a wish for a spot to note something they were worried about, or sad about, or mad about. This reminded me of a spiritual practice based on the work of Saint Ignatius of Loyola that I've often turned to—penning my moment of greatest "consolation" *and* greatest "desolation." In other words, when did I experience the most love, feel the closest to my Creator? And when did I experience the least love, feel the furthest from my best self and my Creator? When was I angry, ashamed, embarrassed, afraid, sad? These moments of desolation are often great opportunities to learn and to grow. So, I decided, rather than label this space for a "highlight," to leave it blank for you. You can fill it with a "desolation" or an affirmation, mantra, or quote you come across that speaks to you, a prayer for yourself or someone else, or anything else you can think of that you'd like to put there.

THE "TAG" PART OF THIS PRACTICE

(This section of the practice was originally inspired by a lesson in an online program given by Christine Kane called Uplevel Your Life®. I've adapted her process quite a bit over the years.)

You could, if you like this metaphor, consider the "Thanks-Giving" and "Gratitude" parts of *TAG, I'M IT!* as the bread in an "appreciation sandwich" that nourishes us bountifully. I've always loved the story in the Book of Exodus about the manna God provided to Moses and the Israelites in the desert each day. So, I think of the goodness and gifts we receive daily as our form of manna (bread). When we take the time to take in the love in our lives, as well as the multitude of comforts and gifts that we partake of—and to be thankful and grateful for them—we are, in a real sense, gathering that manna.

Well, then, I wondered, what is sandwiched between these abundant "slices" of love, beauty, and grace at work in our lives? I decided this "filling" is made up of our own accomplishments and actions, both large and small, through which we contribute our gifts to the world, nourishing others. If you're like me, you find it much easier to appreciate what you receive than what you give. But I've learned that taking a few moments to note what we've achieved and accomplished pays rich dividends.

Here's a TAG breakdown, by letter:

Thanks-Giving

Note three simple comforts or pleasures that y*our ordinary, daily life hold*s, such as good friends and loving family members, running water, a car that works, everyday sensory delights (like a cup of tea or coffee in your favorite mug or a beautiful sunset). Consider the "underpinnings" of your good life as well. Who or what sustains you? Whose love and generosity contributed to who you are, what you have, and what you do?

Thankfulness is a great energy that allows you to connect with your happiest, most creative self. Naming even a few of the good things in your life invites more good. It also lifts the heart, taps into positive emotion and provides solid, loving, nurturing ground to stand on each day.

Notice the good that you take completely for granted. (For example, I never offered thanks for having running water in our kitchen sink until it clogged and the plumber couldn't come for a few days.) Write down a good friend's name, the fact that there are people in the world who love you just as you are. Don't forget your thankfulness for what you hear, see, taste, touch, and smell: a favorite song, a cat's purr, a mockingbird trill. A crisp Winesap apple. The smell of rosemary rubbed between your fingers. Crisp, clean sheets. A dogwood in bloom. A photo that reminds you of a special trip and/or of someone you love.

Beyond pleasures and comforts, contemplate the source of the goodness in your life, too. Can you connect with a sense of awe and wonder for your life itself? For the opportunity each day to manifest love, and to receive it? To grow in wisdom?

Act-Knowledge-ment of Your Accomplishments and Actions

Note three instances in which you've been of service to others, achieved success, or acted on behalf of one of your own dreams or goals.

This funny spelling of the word *acknowledgment* is a bit of wordplay that came about one morning when I noticed that *acknowledgment* has at its core the words *act* and *knowledge*—along with a suffix that denotes an action or resulting state. Aha! To acknowledge ourselves, I realized, is to give ourselves the knowledge that we *have* acted. Given that I so often berate myself for what I DON'T accomplish rather than celebrating what I actually DO, this shift is heartening. The beauty of noting what I accomplish through this list of "Ta-done's" (as opposed to "To-do's") is that I now spend more of my time mindfully, and productively, doing what I can.

What did you do today that made your corner of the world a little better? To whom did you offer a needed smile or a kindness? What useful end did you work toward, at work or at home? What healthy habits did you engage in? How did you add beauty and/or order to life? (Yes, even cleaning out your refrigerator or garage is, as my dad used to say, "a contribution to better living.") As well as noting your service to others, give yourself "the knowledge that you have acted" on behalf of one of your own dreams or goals. And if you haven't, what could you do tomorrow? (You can make this an item on your "I'M IT!" list.) And don't forget that *how you're being* is as important as *what you're doing*. It's an accomplishment to be patient and cheerful when what you feel like doing is biting someone's head off!

If one of your dreams is writing, take Miller Williams's advice to "First, notice everything": paying attention to the specific details of your life counts! So does reading good writing, crafting a few beautiful sentences, revising, meeting with a writer friend, ten minutes listing what to write about . . .

Gratitude for Gifts Received

Note three unexpected gifts of the day, tangible or intangible, that you're grateful for, such as compliments, kindnesses, opportunities, or synchronicities.

Yes, gifts are things we're thankful for. But there is a difference between Thanks-Giving for the good our "ordinary" lives hold and Gratitude for specific Gifts received. Gifts can be physical objects, but they can also come in the form of affirming words, experiences, kindnesses large and small, serendipities and synchronicities that let us know Divine Love (or the Universe, or a creative source, depending on your beliefs) is guiding our lives. A parking spot close to the grocery store when it's raining is a gift. So is a compliment, whether it comes in a text, in an email, or in-person. The more you pay attention, the more you'll notice the gifts that are being given to you through a multitude of sources.

In the writing realm, gifts can manifest in numerous ways, such as unexpected opportunities, positive feedback on our work, and ideas that burst forth in our own imaginations or around us—like an overheard bit of dialogue that fixes a scene or a phrase you read in a poem that reminds us of something we want to write about.

Lastly, here are a few words about the important final step, "I'm It":

. . . I'M IT!

Choose the three most-important-to-you actions you will take tomorrow. based on your deepest commitments and what will inspire the most love, peace, and fulfillment.

When it comes to crafting meaningful work, living a healthy lifestyle, building rewarding relationships, reaching our goals, and fulfilling our dreams, each of us is IT!

Yes, we all deserve rich support, to seek and accept help. But no one can cause your success but you. Only you can determine how to best live out your vocation, which Frederick Buechner defines as that intersection "where your greatest joy meets the world's greatest need."

As legendary choreographer Martha Graham said, "There is a vitality, a life force, an energy, a quickening that is translated through you into action, and because there is only one of you in all of time, this expression is unique. And if you block it, it will never exist through any other medium and it will be lost. The world will not have it. It is not your business to determine how good it is nor how valuable nor how it compares with other expressions. It is your business to keep it yours clearly and directly, to keep the channel open."

Each new day is an opportunity to "keep the channel open," to connect with the best within us and without us, to mindfully choose what matters most. Yes, it takes courage to be the one to select, deliberately, only a few actions to positively commit to from the myriad of possibilities. But take heart. Take on being the one holding the reins of your life. Practice patience: some of our most desired outcomes can only be reached by taking one small step after another, and another . . . And much of our happiness comes from tending the love and beauty that is already ours.

May this *TAG, I'M IT!* journal adds joy and meaning to your days.

One last tip: Invite a friend or family member to embark upon this process with you. Share the best of your thanks-giving, act-knowledge-ments, and gifts with each other. You'll be spreading thankfulness and gratitude as you do, as well as adding to your own. As a Swedish proverb says, "Shared joy is double joy; Shared sorrow is half a sorrow."

Write it on your heart
that every day is the best day in the year.
He is rich who owns the day, and no one owns the day
who allows it to be invaded with fret and anxiety.

Finish every day and be done with it.
You have done what you could.
Some blunders and absurdities, no doubt crept in.
Forget them as soon as you can, tomorrow is a new day;
begin it well and serenely, with too high a spirit
to be cumbered with your old nonsense.

This new day is too dear,
with its hopes and invitations,
to waste a moment on the yesterdays.

~ Ralph Waldo Emerson

TODAY'S DATE:

T

Thanks-Giving

A

Act-Knowledge-ments

G

Gifts

The world needs your gifts as much as you need to give them.

~ Sarah Ban Breathnach

I'm "It"

The three most-important-to-me things I will do tomorrow:

TODAY'S DATE:

T
Thanks-Giving

A
Act-Knowledge-ments

G
Gifts

The journey of a thousand miles begins with a single step.

~ Lao Tzu

I'm "It"

The three most-important-to-me things I will do tomorrow:

T

Thanks-Giving

A

Act-Knowledge-ments

G

Gifts

I would maintain that thanks are the highest form of thought; and that gratitude is happiness doubled by wonder.

~ G.K. Chesterton

I'm "It"

The three most-important-to-me things I will do tomorrow:

TODAY'S DATE:

T

Thanks-Giving

A

Act-Knowledge-ments

G

Gifts

Reflect upon your present blessings, of which every man has plenty; not on your past misfortunes, of which all men have some.

~ Charles Dickens

I'm "It"

The three most-important-to-me things I will do tomorrow:

TODAY'S DATE:

T
Thanks-Giving

A
Act-Knowledge-ments

G
Gifts

Wake at dawn with a winged heart and give thanks for another day of loving.

~ Khalil Gibran

I'm "It"

The three most-important-to-me things I will do tomorrow:

TODAY'S DATE:

T
Thanks-Giving

A
Act-Knowledge-ments

G
Gifts

In ordinary life, we hardly realize that we receive a great deal more than we give, and that it is only with gratitude that life becomes rich.

~ Dietrich Bonhoeffer

I'm "It"

The three most-important-to-me things I will do tomorrow:

TODAY'S DATE:

T
Thanks-Giving

A
Act-Knowledge-ments

G
Gifts

To read a poem in January is as lovely as to go for a walk in June.

~ Jean-Paul Sartre

I'm "It"

The three most-important-to-me things I will do tomorrow:

T
Thanks-Giving

A
Act-Knowledge-ments

G
Gifts

Imagination is more important than knowledge.

~ Albert Einstein

I'm "It"
The three most-important-to-me things I will do tomorrow:

TODAY'S DATE:

T
Thanks-Giving

A
Act-Knowledge-ments

G
Gifts

Gratitude turns what we have into enough, and more. It turns denial into acceptance, chaos into order, confusion into clarity...it makes sense of our past, brings peace for today, and creates a vision for tomorrow.

~ Melody Beattie

I'm "It"
The three most-important-to-me things I will do tomorrow:

TODAY'S DATE:

T
Thanks-Giving

A
Act-Knowledge-ments

G
Gifts

To achieve great things, two things are needed: a plan, and not quite enough time.

~ Leonard Bernstein

I'm "It"
The three most-important-to-me things I will do tomorrow:

T
Thanks-Giving

A
Act-Knowledge-ments

G
Gifts

Whether it's the best of times or the worst of times, it's the only time we've got.

~ Art Buchwald

I'm "It"

The three most-important-to-me things I will do tomorrow:

TODAY'S DATE:

T

Thanks-Giving

A

Act-Knowledge-ments

G

Gifts

Piglet noticed that even though he had a Very Small Heart, it could hold a rather large ''amount of Gratitude.

~ A.A. Milne

I'm "It"

The three most-important-to-me things I will do tomorrow:

TODAY'S DATE:

T

Thanks-Giving

A

Act-Knowledge-ments

G

Gifts

In life, one has a choice to take one of two paths: to wait for some special day—or to celebrate each special day.

~ Rasheed Ogunlaru

I'm "It"

The three most-important-to-me things I will do tomorrow:

TODAY'S DATE:

T

Thanks-Giving

A

Act-Knowledge-ments

G

Gifts

If only I may grow: firmer, simpler, quieter, warmer.

~ Dag Hammarskjold

I'm "It"

The three most-important-to-me things I will do tomorrow:

TODAY'S DATE:

T
Thanks-Giving

A
Act-Knowledge-ments

G
Gifts

Maybe our world will grow kinder eventually./Maybe the desire to make something beautiful/is the piece of God that is inside each of us.

~ Mary Oliver in "Franz Marc's Blue Horses"

I'm "It"

The three most-important-to-me things I will do tomorrow:

TODAY'S DATE:

T
Thanks-Giving

A
Act-Knowledge-ments

G
Gifts

Acknowledging the good that you already have in your life is the foundation for all abundance.

~ Eckhart Tolle

I'm "It"
The three most-important-to-me things I will do tomorrow:

TODAY'S DATE:

T
Thanks-Giving

A
Act-Knowledge-ments

G
Gifts

You can't study the map forever. At some point it's time to start walking; there is only so much daylight.

~ Rob Lowe

I'm "It"
The three most-important-to-me things I will do tomorrow:

TODAY'S DATE:

T

Thanks-Giving

A

Act-Knowledge-ments

G

Gifts

Be still, and the world is bound to turn herself inside out to entertain you. Everywhere you look, joyful noise is clanging to drown out quiet desperation.

~ Barbara Kingsolver

I'm "It"

The three most-important-to-me things I will do tomorrow:

TODAY'S DATE:

T
Thanks-Giving

A
Act-Knowledge-ments

G
Gifts

If you want to turn your life around, try thankfulness. It will change your life mightily.

~ Gerald Good

I'm "It"
The three most-important-to-me things I will do tomorrow:

T
Thanks-Giving

A
Act-Knowledge-ments

G
Gifts

We should certainly count our blessings, but we should also make our blessings count.

~ Neal A. Maxwell

I'm "It"

The three most-important-to-me things I will do tomorrow:

TODAY'S DATE:

T
Thanks-Giving

A
Act-Knowledge-ments

G
Gifts

As we express our gratitude, we must never forget that the highest appreciation is not to utter words but to live by them.

~ John F. Kennedy

I'm "It"
The three most-important-to-me things I will do tomorrow:

TODAY'S DATE:

T
Thanks-Giving

A
Act-Knowledge-ments

G
Gifts

The world has enough beautiful mountains and meadows . . . It has plenty of stars and the promise of a new sunrise and sunset every day. What the world needs more of is people to appreciate and enjoy it.

~ Michael Josephson

I'm "It"

The three most-important-to-me things I will do tomorrow:

TODAY'S DATE:

T
Thanks-Giving

A
Act-Knowledge-ments

G
Gifts

No one who achieves success does so without acknowledging the help of others. The wise and confident acknowledge this help with gratitude.

~ Alfred North Whitehead

I'm "It"
The three most-important-to-me things I will do tomorrow:

TODAY"S DATE:

T

Thanks-Giving

A

Act-Knowledge-ments

G

Gifts

Gratitude is not only the greatest of virtues but the parent of all others.

~ Cicero

I'm "It"

The three most-important-to-me things I will do tomorrow:

TODAY'S DATE:

T
Thanks-Giving

A
Act-Knowledge-ments

G
Gifts

This a wonderful day. I've never seen this one before.

~ Maya Angelou

I'm "It"

The three most-important-to-me things I will do tomorrow:

TODAY'S DATE:

T

Thanks-Giving

A

Act-Knowledge-ments

G

Gifts

To move the world, we must first move ourselves.

~ Socrates

I'm "It"

The three most-important-to-me things I will do tomorrow:

TODAY'S DATE:

T
Thanks-Giving

A
Act-Knowledge-ments

G
Gifts

Learn to say 'no' to the good so you can say 'yes' to the best.

~ John C. Maxwell

I'm "It"
The three most-important-to-me things I will do tomorrow:

TODAY'S DATE:

T
Thanks-Giving

A
Act-Knowledge-ments

G
Gifts

Caress the detail, the divine detail.

~ Vladimir Nabokov

I'm "It"

The three most-important-to-me things I will do tomorrow:

TODAY'S DATE:

T
Thanks-Giving

A
Act-Knowledge-ments

G
Gifts

It is necessary to write, if the days are not to slip emptily by. How else, indeed, to clap the net over the butterfly of the moment?

~ Vita Sackville-West

I'm "It"

The three most-important-to-me things I will do tomorrow:

TODAY'S DATE:

T
Thanks-Giving

A
Act-Knowledge-ments

G
Gifts

Magical things happen every day, if we allow it. Think of daylight, of the stars at night, a flower. A dandelion is a miracle.

~ Pamela Travers

I'm "It"

The three most-important-to-me things I will do tomorrow:

TODAY'S DATE:

T
Thanks-Giving

A
Act-Knowledge-ments

G
Gifts

We keep each other alive with our stories. We need to share them, as much as we need to share food.

~ Barry Lopez

I'm "It"

The three most-important-to-me things I will do tomorrow:

TODAY'S DATE:

T
Thanks-Giving

A
Act-Knowledge-ments

G
Gifts

Faith is taking the first step even when you don't see the whole staircase.

~ Martin Luther King, Jr.

I'm "It"

The three most-important-to-me things I will do tomorrow:

TODAY'S DATE:

T

Thanks-Giving

A

Act-Knowledge-ments

G

Gifts

If you do not practice gratefulness, its benefaction will go unnoticed, and your capacity to draw on its gifts will be diminished. To be grateful is to find blessings in everything.

~ Alan Cohen

I'm "It"

The three most-important-to-me things I will do tomorrow:

TODAY'S DATE:

T
Thanks-Giving

A
Act-Knowledge-ments

G
Gifts

Enjoy the little things, for one day you may look back and realize they were the big things.

~ Robert Brault

I'm "It"
The three most-important-to-me things I will do tomorrow:

TODAY'S DATE:

T
Thanks-Giving

A
Act-Knowledge-ments

G
Gifts

Ease up on yourselves. Have some compassion for yourself as well as for others. There's no such thing as perfection, and life is not a race.

~ Doug Marlette

I'm "It"

The three most-important-to-me things I will do tomorrow:

TODAY'S DATE:

T	A	G
Thanks-Giving	Act-Knowledge-ments	Gifts

Appreciation is a wonderful thing:
It makes what is excellent in others
belong to us as well.

~ Voltaire

I'm "It"

The three most-important-to-me things I will do tomorrow:

TODAY'S DATE:

T
Thanks-Giving

A
Act-Knowledge-ments

G
Gifts

Beauty saves. Beauty heals. Beauty motivates. Beauty unites. Beauty returns us to our origins, and here lies the ultimate act of saving, of healing, of overcoming dualism. Beauty allows us to forget the pain and dwell on the joy.

~ Matthew Fox

I'm "It"

The three most-important-to-me things I will do tomorrow:

TODAY'S DATE:

T
Thanks-Giving

A
Act-Knowledge-ments

G
Gifts

One forges one's style on the terrible anvil of daily dead-lines . . . The artist is nothing without the gift, but the gift is nothing without work.

~ Émile Zola

I'm "It"

The three most-important-to-me things I will do tomorrow:

TODAY'S DATE:

T
Thanks-Giving

A
Act-Knowledge-ments

G
Gifts

I truly believe we can either see the connections, celebrate them, and express gratitude for our blessings, or we can see life as a string of coincidences that have no meaning or connection. For me, I'm going to believe in miracles. . . .

~ Mike Ericksen

I'm "It"

The three most-important-to-me things I will do tomorrow:

TODAY'S DATE:

T
Thanks-Giving

A
Act-Knowledge-ments

G
Gifts

I wake each morning with a desire to save the world and a desire to savor the world; this makes it hard to plan the day.

~ E. B. White

I'm "It"
The three most-important-to-me things I will do tomorrow:

TODAY'S DATE:

T
Thanks-Giving

A
Act-Knowledge-ments

G
Gifts

Your vocation in life is where your greatest joy meets the world's greatest need.

~ Frederick Buechner

I'm "It"

The three most-important-to-me things I will do tomorrow:

T

Thanks-Giving

A

Act-Knowledge-ments

G

Gifts

*It is not joy that makes us grateful,
it is gratitude that makes us joyful.*

~ David Steindl-Rast

I'm "It"

The three most-important-to-me things I will do tomorrow:

TODAY'S DATE:

T

Thanks-Giving

A

Act-Knowledge-ments

G

Gifts

'Enough' is a feast.

~ Buddhist proverb

I'm "It"

The three most-important-to-me things I will do tomorrow:

TODAY'S DATE:

T
Thanks-Giving

A
Act-Knowledge-ments

G
Gifts

You don't have to be great to start, but you have to start to be great.

~ Joe Sabah

I'm "It"

The three most-important-to-me things I will do tomorrow:

TODAY'S DATE:

T
Thanks-Giving

A
Act-Knowledge-ments

G
Gifts

If you want to find happiness, find gratitude.

~ Steve Maraboli

I'm "It"
The three most-important-to-me things I will do tomorrow:

TODAY'S DATE:

T
Thanks-Giving

A
Act-Knowledge-ments

G
Gifts

One ought, every day at least, to hear a little song, read a good poem, see a fine picture, and, if it were possible, to speak a few reasonable words.

~ Johann Wolfgang von Goethe

I'm "It"

The three most-important-to-me things I will do tomorrow:

TODAY'S DATE:

T

Thanks-Giving

A

Act-Knowledge-ments

G

Gifts

Who among us will refuse to buy into the conspiracy of this world that asks us to play small?

~ Elliot Sobel

I'm "It"

The three most-important-to-me things I will do tomorrow:

TODAY'S DATE:

T
Thanks-Giving

A
Act-Knowledge-ments

G
Gifts

Why not go out on a limb?
That's where the fruit is.

~ Mark Twain

I'm "It"
The three most-important-to-me things I will do tomorrow:

T
Thanks-Giving

A
Act-Knowledge-ments

G
Gifts

If you want something you never had, you have to do something you've never done.

~ Thomas Jefferson

I'm "It"
The three most-important-to-me things I will do tomorrow:

TODAY'S DATE:

T

Thanks-Giving

A

Act-Knowledge-ments

G

Gifts

If one advances confidently in the direction of his dreams, and endeavors to live the life which he has imagined, he will meet with a success unexpected in common hours.

~ Henry David Thoreau

I'm "It"

The three most-important-to-me things I will do tomorrow:

TODAY'S DATE:

T
Thanks-Giving

A
Act-Knowledge-ments

G
Gifts

The real voyage of discovery consists not in seeking new landscapes, but in having new eyes.

~ Marcel Proust

I'm "It"
The three most-important-to-me things I will do tomorrow:

TODAY'S DATE:

T
Thanks-Giving

A
Act-Knowledge-ments

G
Gifts

Seeds of discouragement will not grow in the thankful heart.

~ Anonymous

I'm "It"
The three most-important-to-me things I will do tomorrow:

TODAY'S DATE:

T
Thanks-Giving

A
Act-Knowledge-ments

G
Gifts

If we have listening ears, God speaks to us in our own language, whatever that language is.

~ Mahatma Gandhi

I'm "It"

The three most-important-to-me things I will do tomorrow:

TODAY'S DATE:

T
Thanks-Giving

A
Act-Knowledge-ments

G
Gifts

To fill the hour and leave no crevice . . . that is happiness.

~ Ralph Waldo Emerson

I'm "It"

The three most-important-to-me things I will do tomorrow:

TODAY'S DATE:

T

Thanks-Giving

A

Act-Knowledge-ments

G

Gifts

The most wasted of all days is one without laughter.

~ e. e. cummings

I'm "It"

The three most-important-to-me things I will do tomorrow:

TODAY'S DATE:

T
Thanks-Giving

A
Act-Knowledge-ments

G
Gifts

A musician must make music, an artist must paint, an poet must write, if he is to be ultimately at peace with himself.

~ Abraham Maslow

I'm "It"
The three most-important-to-me things I will do tomorrow:

TODAY'S DATE:

T

Thanks-Giving

A

Act-Knowledge-ments

G

Gifts

Happiness is itself a kind of gratitude.

~ Anonymous

I'm "It"

The three most-important-to-me things I will do tomorrow:

TODAY'S DATE:

T
Thanks-Giving

A
Act-Knowledge-ments

G
Gifts

The best things are nearest: breath in your nostrils, light in your eyes, flowers at your feet, duties at your hand, the path of God just before you.

~ Robert Louis Stevenson

I'm "It"

The three most-important-to-me things I will do tomorrow:

TODAY'S DATE:

T
Thanks-Giving

A
Act-Knowledge-ments

G
Gifts

Before you can be creative,
you must be courageous.
Creativity is the destination,
but courage is the journey.

~ Joey Reiman

I'm "It"

The three most-important-to-me things I will do tomorrow:

TODAY'S DATE:

T
Thanks-Giving

A
Act-Knowledge-ments

G
Gifts

You were not born empty. You inherited a thousand generations of wisdom, skill, poetry, song, all the sunrises and sunsets of knowledge past. You are the sum of all the people who went before you.

~ Bryce Courtenay

I'm "It"

The three most-important-to-me things I will do tomorrow:

T

Thanks-Giving

A

Act-Knowledge-ments

G

Gifts

*Find what brings you joy and
go there. The Muse lingers
near the home of our joy.*

~ Jan Phillips

I'm "It"

The three most-important-to-me things I will do tomorrow:

TODAY'S DATE:

T
Thanks-Giving

A
Act-Knowledge-ments

G
Gifts

Decision is the spark that ignites action. Until a decision is made nothing happens.

~ Wilfred A. Peterson

I'm "It"

The three most-important-to-me things I will do tomorrow:

T
Thanks-Giving

A
Act-Knowledge-ments

G
Gifts

Write what should not be forgotten....

~ Isabel Allende

I'm "It"
The three most-important-to-me things I will do tomorrow:

TODAY'S DATE:

T
Thanks-Giving

A
Act-Knowledge-ments

G
Gifts

There is a way that nature speaks, that land speaks. Most of the time we are simply not patient enough, quiet enough, to pay attention to the story.

~ Linda Hogan

I'm "It"
The three most-important-to-me things I will do tomorrow:

TODAY'S DATE:

T
Thanks-Giving

A
Act-Knowledge-ments

G
Gifts

The way to develop the best that is in a person is by appreciation and encouragement.

~ Charles Schwab

I'm "It"

The three most-important-to-me things I will do tomorrow:

TODAY'S DATE:

T
Thanks-Giving

A
Act-Knowledge-ments

G
Gifts

Just as each cell contains our whole being, so each thought and dream contains our whole self, too. If our dreams weren't already real within us, we could not even dream them.

~ Gloria Steinem

I'm "It"

The three most-important-to-me things I will do tomorrow:

TODAY'S DATE:

T
Thanks-Giving

A
Act-Knowledge-ments

G
Gifts

Most folks are about as happy as they make up their minds to be.

~ Abraham Lincoln

I'm "It"

The three most-important-to-me things I will do tomorrow:

TODAY'S DATE:

T
Thanks-Giving

A
Act-Knowledge-ments

G
Gifts

Never lose sight of the fact that the most important yardstick of your success will be how you treat other people.

~ Barbara Bush

I'm "It"

The three most-important-to-me things I will do tomorrow:

TODAY'S DATE:

T

Thanks-Giving

A

Act-Knowledge-ments

G

Gifts

My day begins and ends with gratitude.

~ Louise Hay

I'm "It"

The three most-important-to-me things I will do tomorrow:

TODAY'S DATE:

T
Thanks-Giving

A
Act-Knowledge-ments

G
Gifts

Everybody is talented, original and has something important to say.

~ Brenda Ueland

I'm "It"
The three most-important-to-me things I will do tomorrow:

TODAY'S DATE:

T

Thanks-Giving

A

Act-Knowledge-ments

G

Gifts

To live a creative life, we must lose our fear of being wrong.

~ Joseph Chilton Pearce

I'm "It"

The three most-important-to-me things I will do tomorrow:

TODAY'S DATE:

T
Thanks-Giving

A
Act-Knowledge-ments

G
Gifts

The more grateful I am, the more beauty I see.

~ Mary Davis

I'm "It"
The three most-important-to-me things I will do tomorrow:

TODAY'S DATE:

T
Thanks-Giving

A
Act-Knowledge-ments

G
Gifts

If you don't think every day is a good day, just try missing one.

Cavett Robert

I'm "It"
The three most-important-to-me things I will do tomorrow:

TODAY'S DATE:

T
Thanks-Giving

A
Act-Knowledge-ments

G
Gifts

The future is not some place we are going, but one we are creating. The paths are not to be found, but made. And the activity of making them changes both the maker and their destination.

~ John Schaar

I'm "It"
The three most-important-to-me things I will do tomorrow:

TODAY'S DATE:

T
Thanks-Giving

A
Act-Knowledge-ments

G
Gifts

If more of us valued food and cheer and song above hoarded gold, it would be a merrier world.

~ J.R.R. Tolkien

I'm "It"

The three most-important-to-me things I will do tomorrow:

TODAY'S DATE:

T
Thanks-Giving

A
Act-Knowledge-ments

G
Gifts

Great things are not accomplished by those who yield to trends and fads and popular opinion.

~ Jack Kerouac

I'm "It"
The three most-important-to-me things I will do tomorrow:

TODAY'S DATE:

T
Thanks-Giving

A
Act-Knowledge-ments

G
Gifts

Gratitude is the experience of our true self.

~ Gina Lake

I'm "It"

The three most-important-to-me things I will do tomorrow:

TODAY'S DATE:

T
Thanks-Giving

A
Act-Knowledge-ments

G
Gifts

The roots of all goodness lie in the soil of appreciation.

~ the 14th Dalai Lama

I'm "It"
The three most-important-to-me things I will do tomorrow:

TODAY'S DATE:

T

Thanks-Giving

A

Act-Knowledge-ments

G

Gifts

All the way to heaven is heaven.

~ Catherine of Sienna

I'm "It"

The three most-important-to-me things I will do tomorrow:

T
Thanks-Giving

A
Act-Knowledge-ments

G
Gifts

Letting your mind play is the best way to solve problems.

~ Bill Watterson

I'm "It"

The three most-important-to-me things I will do tomorrow:

TODAY'S DATE:

T
Thanks-Giving

A
Act-Knowledge-ments

G
Gifts

We can complain because rose bushes have thorns, or rejoice because thorns have roses.

~ Alphonse Karr

I'm "It"

The three most-important-to-me things I will do tomorrow:

TODAY'S DATE:

T

Thanks-Giving

A

Act-Knowledge-ments

G

Gifts

A sense of blessedness comes from a change of heart, not from more blessings.

~ Mason Cooley

I'm "It"

The three most-important-to-me things I will do tomorrow:

TODAY'S DATE:

T
Thanks-Giving

A
Act-Knowledge-ments

G
Gifts

When you play it too safe, you're taking the biggest risk of your life. Time is the only wealth we're given.

~ Barbara Sher

I'm "It"

The three most-important-to-me things I will do tomorrow:

TODAY'S DATE:

T
Thanks-Giving

A
Act-Knowledge-ments

G
Gifts

We often take for granted the very things that most deserve our gratitude.

~ Cynthia Ozick

I'm "It"

The three most-important-to-me things I will do tomorrow:

TODAY'S DATE:

T
Thanks-Giving

A
Act-Knowledge-ments

G
Gifts

Let us rise up and be thankful, for if we didn't learn a lot today, at least we learned a little, and if we didn't learn a little, at least we didn't get sick, and if we got sick, at least we didn't die; so, let us all be thankful.

~ Buddha

I'm "It"

The three most-important-to-me things I will do tomorrow:

TODAY'S DATE:

T

Thanks-Giving

A

Act-Knowledge-ments

G

Gifts

The thing that is really hard, and really amazing, is giving up on being perfect and beginning the work of becoming yourself.

~ Anna Quindlen

I'm "It"

The three most-important-to-me things I will do tomorrow:

TODAY'S DATE:

T
Thanks-Giving

A
Act-Knowledge-ments

G
Gifts

May the work of your hands be a sign of gratitude and reverence to the human condition.

~ Mahatma Gandhi

I'm "It"

The three most-important-to-me things I will do tomorrow:

TODAY'S DATE:

T
Thanks-Giving

A
Act-Knowledge-ments

G
Gifts

Be thankful for what you have; you'll end up having more. If you concentrate on what you don't have, you will never, ever have enough.

~ Oprah Winfrey

I'm "It"

The three most-important-to-me things I will do tomorrow:

TODAY'S DATE:

T
Thanks-Giving

A
Act-Knowledge-ments

G
Gifts

The quality of a person's life is in direct proportion to their commitment to excellence, regardless of their chosen field of endeavor.

~ Vince Lombardi

I'm "It"

The three most-important-to-me things I will do tomorrow:

TODAY'S DATE:

T
Thanks-Giving

A
Act-Knowledge-ments

G
Gifts

Not what we say about our blessings, but how we use them, is the true measure of our thanksgiving.

~ W. T. Purkiser

I'm "It"

The three most-important-to-me things I will do tomorrow:

TODAY'S DATE:

T
Thanks-Giving

A
Act-Knowledge-ments

G
Gifts

So much has been given to me;
I have no time to ponder over
that which has been denied.

~ Helen Keller

I'm "It"
The three most-important-to-me things I will do tomorrow:

TODAY'S DATE:

T
Thanks-Giving

A
Act-Knowledge-ments

G
Gifts

*If you don't risk anything
you risk even more.*

~ Erica Jong

I'm "It"

The three most-important-to-me things I will do tomorrow:

TODAY'S DATE:

T
Thanks-Giving

A
Act-Knowledge-ments

G
Gifts

When a person doesn't have gratitude, something is missing in his or her humanity.

~ Elie Wiesel

I'm "It"

The three most-important-to-me things I will do tomorrow:

TODAY'S DATE:

T
Thanks-Giving

A
Act-Knowledge-ments

G
Gifts

If a fellow isn't thankful for what he's got, he isn't likely to be thankful for what he's going to get.

~ Frank A. Clark

I'm "It"
The three most-important-to-me things I will do tomorrow:

TODAY'S DATE:

T
Thanks-Giving

A
Act-Knowledge-ments

G
Gifts

He who sows courtesy reaps friendship, and he who plants kindness gathers love.

~ Saint Basil

I'm "It"

The three most-important-to-me things I will do tomorrow:

TODAY'S DATE:

T

Thanks-Giving

A

Act-Knowledge-ments

G

Gifts

Thankfulness is the beginning of gratitude. Gratitude is the completion of thankfulness. Thankfulness may consist merely of words. Gratitude is shown in acts.

~ Henri Frederic Amiel

I'm "It"

The three most-important-to-me things I will do tomorrow:

TODAY'S DATE:

T
Thanks-Giving

A
Act-Knowledge-ments

G
Gifts

The best way to pay for a lovely moment is to enjoy it.

~ Richard Bach

I'm "It"

The three most-important-to-me things I will do tomorrow:

TODAY'S DATE:

T

Thanks-Giving

A

Act-Knowledge-ments

G

Gifts

Too many people overvalue what they are not and undervalue what they are.

~ Malcolm Forbes

I'm "It"

The three most-important-to-me things I will do tomorrow:

TODAY'S DATE:

T
Thanks-Giving

A
Act-Knowledge-ments

G
Gifts

Nothing is more honorable than a grateful heart.

~ Lucius Annaeus Seneca

I'm "It"

The three most-important-to-me things I will do tomorrow:

TODAY'S DATE:

T
Thanks-Giving

A
Act-Knowledge-ments

G
Gifts

Such things. . . as the grasp of a child's hand in your own, the flavor of an apple, . . . the sunlight on rock and leaves, the feel of music, the bark of a tree, . . . the face of the wind—what else is there? What else do we need?

~ Edward Abbey

I'm "It"

The three most-important-to-me things I will do tomorrow:

T
Thanks-Giving

A
Act-Knowledge-ments

G
Gifts

Success is going from failure to failure with no loss of enthusiasm.

~ Winston Churchill

I'm "It"

The three most-important-to-me things I will do tomorrow:

TODAY'S DATE:

T
Thanks-Giving

A
Act-Knowledge-ments

G
Gifts

Adversity reveals genius, prosperity conceals it.

~ Horace

I'm "It"

The three most-important-to-me things I will do tomorrow:

TODAY'S DATE:

T
Thanks-Giving

A
Act-Knowledge-ments

G
Gifts

Why not seize the pleasure at once? How often is happiness destroyed by preparation, foolish preparation!

~ Jane Austen

I'm "It"
The three most-important-to-me things I will do tomorrow:

T

Thanks-Giving

A

Act-Knowledge-ments

G

Gifts

If we had to say what writing is, we would define it essentially as an act of courage.

~ Cynthia Ozick

I'm "It"

The three most-important-to-me things I will do tomorrow:

TODAY'S DATE:

T

Thanks-Giving

A

Act-Knowledge-ments

G

Gifts

What separates privilege from entitlement is gratitude.

~ Brené Brown

I'm "It"

The three most-important-to-me things I will do tomorrow:

TODAY'S DATE:

T

Thanks-Giving

A

Act-Knowledge-ments

G

Gifts

Do not spoil what you have by desiring what you have not; remember that what you now have was once among the things you only hoped for.

~ Epicurus

I'm "It"

The three most-important-to-me things I will do tomorrow:

T

Thanks-Giving

A

Act-Knowledge-ments

G

Gifts

Your vision will become clear only when you look into your heart. Who looks outside, dreams. Who looks inside, awakens.

~ Carl Jung

I'm "It"

The three most-important-to-me things I will do tomorrow:

TODAY'S DATE:

T
Thanks-Giving

A
Act-Knowledge-ments

G
Gifts

Showing gratitude is one of the simplest yet most powerful things humans can do for each other.

~ Randy Pausch

I'm "It"

The three most-important-to-me things I will do tomorrow:

TODAY'S DATE:

T
Thanks-Giving

A
Act-Knowledge-ments

G
Gifts

The smallest act of kindness is worth more than the grandest intention.

~ Oscar Wilde

I'm "It"
The three most-important-to-me things I will do tomorrow:

TODAY'S DATE:

T
Thanks-Giving

A
Act-Knowledge-ments

G
Gifts

What you leave behind is not what is engraved in stone monuments, but what is woven into the lives of others.

~ Pericles

I'm "It"

The three most-important-to-me things I will do tomorrow:

TODAY'S DATE:

T
Thanks-Giving

A
Act-Knowledge-ments

G
Gifts

Mastering others is strength; mastering yourself is true power.

~ Lao Tzu

I'm "It"
The three most-important-to-me things I will do tomorrow:

TODAY'S DATE:

T
Thanks-Giving

A
Act-Knowledge-ments

G
Gifts

Happiness cannot be traveled to, owned, earned, worn or consumed. Happiness is the spiritual experience of living every minute with love, grace, and gratitude.

~ Denis Waitley

I'm "It"

The three most-important-to-me things I will do tomorrow:

TODAY'S DATE:

T
Thanks-Giving

A
Act-Knowledge-ments

G
Gifts

There is nothing noble in being superior to your fellow man; true nobility is being superior to your former self.

~ Ernest Hemingway

I'm "It"

The three most-important-to-me things I will do tomorrow:

TODAY'S DATE:

T
Thanks-Giving

A
Act-Knowledge-ments

G
Gifts

Gratitude doesn't change the scenery. It merely washes clean the glass you look through so you can clearly see the colors.

~ Richelle E. Goodrich

I'm "It"

The three most-important-to-me things I will do tomorrow:

TODAY'S DATE:

T
Thanks-Giving

A
Act-Knowledge-ments

G
Gifts

'Thank you' is the best prayer that anyone could say. I say that one a lot. Thank you expresses extreme gratitude, humility, understanding.

~ Alice Walker

I'm "It"

The three most-important-to-me things I will do tomorrow:

TODAY'S DATE:

T
Thanks-Giving

A
Act-Knowledge-ments

G
Gifts

It doesn't matter how slow you go, so long as you don't stop.

~ Confucius

I'm "It"

The three most-important-to-me things I will do tomorrow:

TODAY'S DATE:

T
Thanks-Giving

A
Act-Knowledge-ments

G
Gifts

The deepest craving of human nature is the need to be appreciated.

~ William James

I'm "It"

The three most-important-to-me things I will do tomorrow:

T

Thanks-Giving

A

Act-Knowledge-ments

G

Gifts

Play is the exultation of the possible.

~ Martin Buber

I'm "It"

The three most-important-to-me things I will do tomorrow:

TODAY'S DATE:

T
Thanks-Giving

A
Act-Knowledge-ments

G
Gifts

I am always doing what I cannot do yet, in order to learn how to do it.

~ Vincent Van Gogh

I'm "It"
The three most-important-to-me things I will do tomorrow:

T

Thanks-Giving

A

Act-Knowledge-ments

G

Gifts

Gratitude is the healthiest of all human emotions. The more you express gratitude for what you have, the more likely you will have even more to express gratitude for.

~ Zig Ziglar

I'm "It"

The three most-important-to-me things I will do tomorrow:

TODAY'S DATE:

T
Thanks-Giving

A
Act-Knowledge-ments

G
Gifts

No duty is more urgent than that of returning thanks.

~ James Allen

I'm "It"

The three most-important-to-me things I will do tomorrow:

TODAY'S DATE:

T
Thanks-Giving

A
Act-Knowledge-ments

G
Gifts

The purpose of life is to live it, to taste experience to the utmost, to reach out eagerly and without fear for newer and richer experience.

~ Eleanor Roosevelt

I'm "It"

The three most-important-to-me things I will do tomorrow:

T

Thanks-Giving

A

Act-Knowledge-ments

G

Gifts

Never confuse a single defeat with a final defeat.

~ F. Scott Fitzgerald

I'm "It"

The three most-important-to-me things I will do tomorrow:

TODAY'S DATE:

T
Thanks-Giving

A
Act-Knowledge-ments

G
Gifts

If the only prayer you said in your whole life was "thank you" that would suffice.

~ Meister Eckhart

I'm "It"

The three most-important-to-me things I will do tomorrow:

T

Thanks-Giving

A

Act-Knowledge-ments

G

Gifts

Life shrinks and expands in proportion to one's courage.

~ Anais Nin

I'm "It"

The three most-important-to-me things I will do tomorrow:

TODAY'S DATE:

T
Thanks-Giving

A
Act-Knowledge-ments

G
Gifts

. . . describing it was beyond their powers, the gratitude that spreads through your body when a burden gets lifted, and the sense of homecoming that follows, when you suddenly remember what it feels like to be yourself.

~ Tom Perrotta

I'm "It"
The three most-important-to-me things I will do tomorrow:

TODAY'S DATE:

T

Thanks-Giving

A

Act-Knowledge-ments

G

Gifts

A mind that is stretched by a new idea can never go back to its original dimensions.

~ Oliver Wendell Holmes

I'm "It"

The three most-important-to-me things I will do tomorrow:

TODAY'S DATE:

T
Thanks-Giving

A
Act-Knowledge-ments

G
Gifts

Real generosity toward the future lies in giving all to the present.

~ Albert Camus

I'm "It"
The three most-important-to-me things I will do tomorrow:

T

Thanks-Giving

A

Act-Knowledge-ments

G

Gifts

When it comes to life the critical thing is whether you take things for granted or take them with gratitude.

~ G.K. Chesterton

I'm "It"

The three most-important-to-me things I will do tomorrow:

TODAY'S DATE:

T
Thanks-Giving

A
Act-Knowledge-ments

G
Gifts

Do you not see how everything that happens keeps on being a beginning?

~ Rainer Maria Rilke

I'm "It"

The three most-important-to-me things I will do tomorrow:

TODAY'S DATE:

T
Thanks-Giving

A
Act-Knowledge-ments

G
Gifts

I'm "It"

Start by doing what's necessary, then what's possible—and suddenly you are doing the impossible.

~ St. Francis of Assisi

The three most-important-to-me things I will do tomorrow:

TODAY'S DATE:

T
Thanks-Giving

A
Act-Knowledge-ments

G
Gifts

At times our own light goes out and is rekindled by a spark from another person. Each of us has cause to think with deep gratitude of those who have lighted the flame within us.

~ Albert Schweitzer

I'm "It"

The three most-important-to-me things I will do tomorrow:

TODAY'S DATE:

T
Thanks-Giving

A
Act-Knowledge-ments

G
Gifts

The main thing in life is not to be afraid to be human.

~ Pablo Casals

I'm "It"

The three most-important-to-me things I will do tomorrow:

TODAY'S DATE:

T
Thanks-Giving

A
Act-Knowledge-ments

G
Gifts

Let the beauty you love be what you do. There are hundreds of ways to kneel and kiss the ground.

~ Rumi

I'm "It"
The three most-important-to-me things I will do tomorrow:

TODAY'S DATE:

T
Thanks-Giving

A
Act-Knowledge-ments

G
Gifts

I'm "It"

The three most-important-to-me things I will do tomorrow:

Gratitude also opens your eyes to the limitless potential of the universe, while dissatisfaction closes your eyes to it.

~ Stephen Richards

TODAY'S DATE:

T
Thanks-Giving

A
Act-Knowledge-ments

G
Gifts

Most of the shadows of this life are caused by standing in our own sunshine.

~ Ralph Waldo Emerson

I'm "It"
The three most-important-to-me things I will do tomorrow:

TODAY'S DATE:

T
Thanks-Giving

A
Act-Knowledge-ments

G
Gifts

I really don't think life is about the I-could-have-beens. Life is only about the I-tried-to-dos. I don't mind the failure, but I can't imagine that I'd forgive myself if I didn't try.

~ Nikki Giovanni

I'm "It"
The three most-important-to-me things I will do tomorrow:

TODAY'S DATE:

T

Thanks-Giving

A

Act-Knowledge-ments

G

Gifts

Gratitude and attitude are not challenges; they are choices.

~ Robert Braathe

I'm "It"

The three most-important-to-me things I will do tomorrow:

TODAY'S DATE:

T
Thanks-Giving

A
Act-Knowledge-ments

G
Gifts

Make it a habit to tell people thank you. To express your appreciation, sincerely and without the expectation of anything in return.

~ Ralph Marston

I'm "It"

The three most-important-to-me things I will do tomorrow:

TODAY'S DATE:

T
Thanks-Giving

A
Act-Knowledge-ments

G
Gifts

Progress always involves risks. You can't steal second base and keep your foot on first.

~ Frederick B. Wilcox

I'm "It"

The three most-important-to-me things I will do tomorrow:

TODAY'S DATE:

T

Thanks-Giving

A

Act-Knowledge-ments

G

Gifts

Count it all joy when you fall into various trials, knowing that the testing of your faith produces patience.

~ The Book of James

I'm "It"

The three most-important-to-me things I will do tomorrow:

TODAY'S DATE:

T
Thanks-Giving

A
Act-Knowledge-ments

G
Gifts

The tragedy of life is not what we suffer, it's what we miss.

~ William James

I'm "It"
The three most-important-to-me things I will do tomorrow:

TODAY'S DATE:

T
Thanks-Giving

A
Act-Knowledge-ments

G
Gifts

I'm "It"

The three most-important-to-me things I will do tomorrow:

We have to do the best we are capable of. This is our sacred human responsibility.

~ Albert Einstein

TODAY'S DATE:

T
Thanks-Giving

A
Act-Knowledge-ments

G
Gifts

Gratitude can transform common days into thanksgiving, turn routine jobs into joy, and change ordinary opportunities into blessings.

~ William Arthur Ward

I'm "It"
The three most-important-to-me things I will do tomorrow:

TODAY'S DATE:

T
Thanks-Giving

A
Act-Knowledge-ments

G
Gifts

The secrets of happiness are to be found in love, children, work and God's created world—singly or in any combination, so your chances are good.

~ Josephine Humphreys

I'm "It"

The three most-important-to-me things I will do tomorrow:

TODAY'S DATE:

T
Thanks-Giving

A
Act-Knowledge-ments

G
Gifts

Brighten the corner where you are..

~ Ina Mae Duley Ogdon

I'm "It"

The three most-important-to-me things I will do tomorrow:

TODAY'S DATE:

T
Thanks-Giving

A
Act-Knowledge-ments

G
Gifts

Divine love blesses all that I think, say, and do.

~ *Daily Word*, a Unity publication

I'm "It"

The three most-important-to-me things I will do tomorrow:

TODAY'S DATE:

T
Thanks-Giving

A
Act-Knowledge-ments

G
Gifts

The best way to know life is to love many things.

~ Vincent Van Gogh

I'm "It"
The three most-important-to-me things I will do tomorrow:

TODAY'S DATE:

T
Thanks-Giving

A
Act-Knowledge-ments

G
Gifts

Success and failure. We think of them as opposites, but they're really not. They're companions - the hero and the sidekick.

~ Jacob A. Riis

I'm "It"

The three most-important-to-me things I will do tomorrow:

TODAY'S DATE:

T
Thanks-Giving

A
Act-Knowledge-ments

G
Gifts

There are always flowers for those who want to see them.

~ Henri Matisse

I'm "It"
The three most-important-to-me things I will do tomorrow:

TODAY'S DATE:

T
Thanks-Giving

A
Act-Knowledge-ments

G
Gifts

When you arise in the morning, think of what a precious privilege it is to be alive -to breathe, to think, to enjoy, to love.

~ Marcus Aurelius

I'm "It"
The three most-important-to-me things I will do tomorrow:

T
Thanks-Giving

A
Act-Knowledge-ments

G
Gifts

To accomplish great things, we must not only act, but also dream; not only plan, but also believe.

~ Anatole France

I'm "It"

The three most-important-to-me things I will do tomorrow:

T
Thanks-Giving

A
Act-Knowledge-ments

G
Gifts

One cannot collect all the beautiful shells on the beach; one can collect only a few, and they are more beautiful if they are few.

~ Anne Morrow Lindbergh

I'm "It"

The three most-important-to-me things I will do tomorrow:

TODAY'S DATE:

T
Thanks-Giving

A
Act-Knowledge-ments

G
Gifts

. . . for the moment you need it, then you bless it —
thank you soup, thank you flashlight—. . .

~ Richard Siken in "Detail of the Hayfield"

I'm "It"

The three most-important-to-me things I will do tomorrow:

TODAY'S DATE:

T
Thanks-Giving

A
Act-Knowledge-ments

G
Gifts

How we spend our days is of course how we spend our lives.

~ Annie Dillard

I'm "It"

The three most-important-to-me things I will do tomorrow:

TODAY'S DATE:

T
Thanks-Giving

A
Act-Knowledge-ments

G
Gifts

When I was eight, I was reading a book in which it was snowing. When I looked outside, I expected there to be snow on the ground. I thought, "This is the most powerful thing I can do! I'm going to be a writer."

~ Candace Bushnell

I'm "It"

The three most-important-to-me things I will do tomorrow:

TODAY'S DATE:

T

Thanks-Giving

A

Act-Knowledge-ments

G

Gifts

We don't see things as they are.
We see them as we are.

~ Anais Nin

I'm "It"

The three most-important-to-me things I will do tomorrow:

TODAY'S DATE:

T
Thanks-Giving

A
Act-Knowledge-ments

G
Gifts

Joy is the simplest form of gratitude.

~ Karl Barth

I'm "It"

The three most-important-to-me things I will do tomorrow:

TODAY'S DATE:

T
Thanks-Giving

A
Act-Knowledge-ments

G
Gifts

Le coeur a ses raisons, que la raison ne connaît point. (The heart has its reasons, of which reason knows nothing.)

~ Blaise Pascal

I'm "It"

The three most-important-to-me things I will do tomorrow:

TODAY'S DATE:

T
Thanks-Giving

A
Act-Knowledge-ments

G
Gifts

Our Town is not offered as a picture of life in a New Hampshire village; it is an attempt to find a value above all price for the smallest events in our daily life.

~ Thornton Wilder

I'm "It"
The three most-important-to-me things I will do tomorrow:

TODAY'S DATE:

T
Thanks-Giving

A
Act-Knowledge-ments

G
Gifts

He who's not busy being born is busy dying.

~ Bob Dylan

I'm "It"

The three most-important-to-me things I will do tomorrow:

TODAY'S DATE:

T
Thanks-Giving

A
Act-Knowledge-ments

G
Gifts

I want to write but more than that I want to bring out all kinds of things that lie buried deep in my heart.

~ Anne Frank

I'm "It"

The three most-important-to-me things I will do tomorrow:

TODAY'S DATE:

T
Thanks-Giving

A
Act-Knowledge-ments

G
Gifts

Real generosity toward the future lies in giving all to the present.

~ Albert Camus

I'm "It"
The three most-important-to-me things I will do tomorrow:

TODAY'S DATE:

T
Thanks-Giving

A
Act-Knowledge-ments

G
Gifts

We are what we repeatedly do.
Excellence then is not an act
but a habit.

~ Aristotle

I'm "It"

The three most-important-to-me things I will do tomorrow:

TODAY'S DATE:

T
Thanks-Giving

A
Act-Knowledge-ments

G
Gifts

Ah, but a man's reach should exceed his grasp, or what's a heaven for?

~ Robert Browning

I'm "It"

The three most-important-to-me things I will do tomorrow:

T

Thanks-Giving

A

Act-Knowledge-ments

G

Gifts

From error to error one discovers the entire truth.

~ Sigmund Freud

I'm "It"

The three most-important-to-me things I will do tomorrow:

T
Thanks-Giving

A
Act-Knowledge-ments

G
Gifts

I exist as I am, that is enough.

~ Walt Whitman

I'm "It"

The three most-important-to-me things I will do tomorrow:

TODAY'S DATE:

T
Thanks-Giving

A
Act-Knowledge-ments

G
Gifts

I write entirely to find out what I'm thinking, what I'm looking at, what I see and what it means. What I want and what I fear.

~ Joan Didion

I'm "It"

The three most-important-to-me things I will do tomorrow:

TODAY'S DATE:

T

Thanks-Giving

A

Act-Knowledge-ments

G

Gifts

Time is the coin of your life. It is the only coin you have, and only you can determine how it will be spent. Be careful lest you let other people spend it for you.

~ Carl Sandburg

I'm "It"

The three most-important-to-me things I will do tomorrow:

TODAY'S DATE:

T
Thanks-Giving

A
Act-Knowledge-ments

G
Gifts

Nothing in this world can take the place of persistence. Talent will not . . . Genius will not . . . Education will not . . . Persistence and determination alone are omnipotent.

~ Calvin Coolidge

I'm "It"

The three most-important-to-me things I will do tomorrow:

TODAY'S DATE:

T
Thanks-Giving

A
Act-Knowledge-ments

G
Gifts

It's never too late to be what you might have been.

~ George Eliot

I'm "It"

The three most-important-to-me things I will do tomorrow:

TODAY'S DATE:

T
Thanks-Giving

A
Act-Knowledge-ments

G
Gifts

The worst that can be said of any of us is: He did not pay attention.

~ William Meredith

I'm "It"
The three most-important-to-me things I will do tomorrow:

TODAY'S DATE:

T

Thanks-Giving

A

Act-Knowledge-ments

G

Gifts

Never for the sake of peace and quiet, deny your own experience or convictions.

~ Dag Hammarskjold

I'm "It"

The three most-important-to-me things I will do tomorrow:

TODAY'S DATE:

T
Thanks-Giving

A
Act-Knowledge-ments

G
Gifts

The future is not some place we are going, but one we are creating. The paths are not to be found, but made. And the activity of making them changes both the maker and their destination.

~ John Schaar

I'm "It"

The three most-important-to-me things I will do tomorrow:

TODAY'S DATE:

T
Thanks-Giving

A
Act-Knowledge-ments

G
Gifts

It's so hard to forget pain, but it's even harder to remember sweetness. We have no scar to show for happiness. We learn so little from peace.

~ Chuck Palahniuk

I'm "It"

The three most-important-to-me things I will do tomorrow:

TODAY'S DATE:

T	A	G
Thanks-Giving	Act-Knowledge-ments	Gifts

The strongest warriors are these two...time and patience.

~ J. Lubbock

I'm "It"

The three most-important-to-me things I will do tomorrow:

TODAY'S DATE:

T
Thanks-Giving

A
Act-Knowledge-ments

G
Gifts

In the end these things matter most: How well did you love? How fully did you live? How deeply did you let go?

~ Siddhartha Gautama

I'm "It"

The three most-important-to-me things I will do tomorrow:

TODAY'S DATE:

T
Thanks-Giving

A
Act-Knowledge-ments

G
Gifts

In ancient China, the Taoists taught that a constant inner smile, a smile to oneself, insured health, happiness and longevity. Why? Smiling to yourself is like basking in love: you become your own best friend. Living with an inner smile is to live in harmony with yourself.

~ Mantak Chia. a Tao Master

I'm "It"

The three most-important-to-me things I will do tomorrow:

TODAY'S DATE:

T
Thanks-Giving

A
Act-Knowledge-ments

G
Gifts

Almost all creativity involves purposeful play.

~ Abraham Maslow

I'm "It"
The three most-important-to-me things I will do tomorrow:

TODAY'S DATE:

T
Thanks-Giving

A
Act-Knowledge-ments

G
Gifts

Kindness is the one commodity of which you should spend more than you earn.

~ T. N. Tiemeyer

I'm "It"

The three most-important-to-me things I will do tomorrow:

TODAY'S DATE:

T

Thanks-Giving

A

Act-Knowledge-ments

G

Gifts

Stop now. Enjoy the moment.
It's now or never.

~ Maxime Lagacé

I'm "It"

The three most-important-to-me things I will do tomorrow:

TODAY'S DATE:

T
Thanks-Giving

A
Act-Knowledge-ments

G
Gifts

Little by little, one travels far.

~ J. R. R. Tolkien

I'm "It"

The three most-important-to-me things I will do tomorrow:

TODAY'S DATE:

T
Thanks-Giving

A
Act-Knowledge-ments

G
Gifts

Rest and be kind, you don't have to prove anything.

~ Jack Kerouac

I'm "It"
The three most-important-to-me things I will do tomorrow:

TODAY'S DATE:

T
Thanks-Giving

A
Act-Knowledge-ments

G
Gifts

The journey not the arrival matters.

~ T.S. Eliot

I'm "It"

The three most-important-to-me things I will do tomorrow:

TODAY'S DATE:

T
Thanks-Giving

A
Act-Knowledge-ments

G
Gifts

A loving heart is the truest wisdom.

~ Charles Dickens

I'm "It"
The three most-important-to-me things I will do tomorrow:

TODAY'S DATE:

T

Thanks-Giving

A

Act-Knowledge-ments

G

Gifts

Be yourself; everyone else is already taken.

~ Oscar Wilde

I'm "It"

The three most-important-to-me things I will do tomorrow:

TODAY'S DATE:

T
Thanks-Giving

A
Act-Knowledge-ments

G
Gifts

The world is full of magic things, patiently waiting for our senses to grow sharper.

~ William Butler Yeats

I'm "It"

The three most-important-to-me things I will do tomorrow:

TODAY'S DATE:

T
Thanks-Giving

A
Act-Knowledge-ments

G
Gifts

We learn to do something by doing it. There is no other way.

~ John Holt

I'm "It"

The three most-important-to-me things I will do tomorrow:

TODAY'S DATE:

T
Thanks-Giving

A
Act-Knowledge-ments

G
Gifts

Whatever course you decide upon, there is always someone to tell you that you are wrong. There are always difficulties arising which tempt you to believe that your critics are right. To map out a course of action and follow it to an end requires courage.

~ Ralph Waldo Emerson

I'm "It"

The three most-important-to-me things I will do tomorrow:

TODAY'S DATE:

T

Thanks-Giving

A

Act-Knowledge-ments

G

Gifts

If the doors of perception were cleansed everything would appear to man as it is: infinite.

~ William Blake

I'm "It"

The three most-important-to-me things I will do tomorrow:

TODAY'S DATE:

T

Thanks-Giving

A

Act-Knowledge-ments

G

Gifts

At the end of the day it's not about what you have or even what you've accomplished... it's about who you've lifted up, who you've made better, it's about what you've given back.

~ Denzel Washington

I'm "It"

The three most-important-to-me things I will do tomorrow:

TODAY'S DATE:

T
Thanks-Giving

A
Act-Knowledge-ments

G
Gifts

Magic is believing in yourself, if you can do that, you can make anything happen.

~ Johann Wolfgang von Goethe

I'm "It"

The three most-important-to-me things I will do tomorrow:

TODAY'S DATE:	

T	A	G
Thanks-Giving	Act-Knowledge-ments	Gifts

An open heart is an open mind.

~ the 14th Dalai Lama

I'm "It"

The three most-important-to-me things I will do tomorrow:

TODAY'S DATE:

T
Thanks-Giving

A
Act-Knowledge-ments

G
Gifts

It is not in the stars to hold our destiny but in ourselves.

~ William Shakespeare

I'm "It"
The three most-important-to-me things I will do tomorrow:

TODAY'S DATE:

T
Thanks-Giving

A
Act-Knowledge-ments

G
Gifts

Life is not about waiting for the storms to pass...it's about learning how to dance in the rain.

~ Jim Rohn

I'm "It"
The three most-important-to-me things I will do tomorrow:

TODAY'S DATE:

T

Thanks-Giving

A

Act-Knowledge-ments

G

Gifts

Eighty percent of success is showing up.

~ Woody Allen

I'm "It"

The three most-important-to-me things I will do tomorrow:

TODAY'S DATE:

T
Thanks-Giving

A
Act-Knowledge-ments

G
Gifts

Every thought is a seed. If you plant crab apples, don't count on harvesting golden delicious.

~ Winston Churchill

I'm "It"

The three most-important-to-me things I will do tomorrow:

TODAY'S DATE:

T
Thanks-Giving

A
Act-Knowledge-ments

G
Gifts

The intuitive mind is a sacred gift and the rational mind is a faithful servant. We have created a society that honors the servant and has forgotten the gift.

~ Albert Einstein

I'm "It"

The three most-important-to-me things I will do tomorrow:

TODAY'S DATE:

T
Thanks-Giving

A
Act-Knowledge-ments

G
Gifts

We cannot live only for ourselves.
A thousand fibers connect us with
our fellow men.

~ Herman Melville

I'm "It"

The three most-important-to-me things I will do tomorrow:

TODAY'S DATE:

T
Thanks-Giving

A
Act-Knowledge-ments

G
Gifts

You see, the human mind is the last great unexplored continent on earth. It contains riches beyond our wildest dreams. It will return anything we want to plant.

~ Earl Nightingale

I'm "It"

The three most-important-to-me things I will do tomorrow:

TODAY'S DATE:

T
Thanks-Giving

A
Act-Knowledge-ments

G
Gifts

Here is the world. Beautiful and terrible things will happen. Don't be afraid.

~ Frederick Buechner

I'm "It"

The three most-important-to-me things I will do tomorrow:

T
Thanks-Giving

A
Act-Knowledge-ments

G
Gifts

You will find poetry nowhere unless you bring some of it with you.

~ Joseph Joubert

I'm "It"

The three most-important-to-me things I will do tomorrow:

TODAY'S DATE:

T

Thanks-Giving

A

Act-Knowledge-ments

G

Gifts

*I don't believe in circumstances.
The people who get on in this
world are the people who get up
and look for the circumstances
they want, and if they can't find
them, they make them.*

~ George Bernard Shaw

I'm "It"

The three most-important-to-me things I will do tomorrow:

TODAY'S DATE:

T

Thanks-Giving

A

Act-Knowledge-ments

G

Gifts

Abandon yourself to the moment, and you will find every day new openings, new light, new insight. And those new insights will go on changing you. One day, suddenly you will see you are each moment new.

~ Osho

I'm "It"

The three most-important-to-me things I will do tomorrow:

TODAY'S DATE:

T

Thanks-Giving

A

Act-Knowledge-ments

G

Gifts

The more you lose yourself in something bigger than yourself, the more energy you will have.

~ Norman Vincent Peale

I'm "It"

The three most-important-to-me things I will do tomorrow:

TODAY'S DATE:

T
Thanks-Giving

A
Act-Knowledge-ments

G
Gifts

Faith is taking the first step even when you don't see the staircase.

~ Bill Meyer

I'm "It"

The three most-important-to-me things I will do tomorrow:

TODAY'S DATE:

T
Thanks-Giving

A
Act-Knowledge-ments

G
Gifts

Though no one an go back and make a brand new start, anyone can start from now and make a brand new ending.

~ Carl Bard

I'm "It"

The three most-important-to-me things I will do tomorrow:

T
Thanks-Giving

A
Act-Knowledge-ments

G
Gifts

Just trust yourself, then you will know how to live.

~ Johann Wolfgang von Goethe

I'm "It"

The three most-important-to-me things I will do tomorrow:

TODAY'S DATE:

T
Thanks-Giving

A
Act-Knowledge-ments

G
Gifts

The only true happiness comes from squandering ourselves for a purpose.

~ William Cowper

I'm "It"

The three most-important-to-me things I will do tomorrow:

TODAY'S DATE:

T
Thanks-Giving

A
Act-Knowledge-ments

G
Gifts

The most wasted of all days is one without laughter.

~ Nicolas Chamfort

I'm "It"
The three most-important-to-me things I will do tomorrow:

TODAY'S DATE:

T
Thanks-Giving

A
Act-Knowledge-ments

G
Gifts

If you make friends with yourself you will never be alone.

~ Maxwell Maltz

I'm "It"
The three most-important-to-me things I will do tomorrow:

TODAY'S DATE:

T
Thanks-Giving

A
Act-Knowledge-ments

G
Gifts

Your work is to discover your work and then with all your heart to give yourself to it.

~ Buddha

I'm "It"

The three most-important-to-me things I will do tomorrow:

TODAY'S DATE:

T
Thanks-Giving

A
Act-Knowledge-ments

G
Gifts

Traveler, there is no path.
The path is made by walking.

~ Antonio Machado in
"XXIX." *Border of a*
Dream: Selected Poems

I'm "It"

The three most-important-to-me things I will do tomorrow:

TODAY'S DATE:

T
Thanks-Giving

A
Act-Knowledge-ments

G
Gifts

Don't judge each day by the harvest you reap but by the seeds that you plant.

~ Robert Louis Stevenson

I'm "It"
The three most-important-to-me things I will do tomorrow:

TODAY'S DATE:

T
Thanks-Giving

A
Act-Knowledge-ments

G
Gifts

Whether you think you can or think you can't—you are right.

~ Henry Ford

I'm "It"
The three most-important-to-me things I will do tomorrow:

TODAY'S DATE:

T
Thanks-Giving

A
Act-Knowledge-ments

G
Gifts

Your labor is your contribution to the miracle.

~ Elizabeth Gilbert

I'm "It"

The three most-important-to-me things I will do tomorrow:

TODAY'S DATE:

T
Thanks-Giving

A
Act-Knowledge-ments

G
Gifts

Take rest; a field that has rested gives a bountiful crop.

~ Ovid

I'm "It"
The three most-important-to-me things I will do tomorrow:

TODAY'S DATE:

T
Thanks-Giving

A
Act-Knowledge-ments

G
Gifts

Unless you try to do something beyond what you have already mastered, you will never grow.

~ Ronald E. Osborn

I'm "It"

The three most-important-to-me things I will do tomorrow:

TODAY'S DATE:

T

Thanks-Giving

A

Act-Knowledge-ments

G

Gifts

Difficult roads often lead to beautiful destinations. The best is yet to come.

~ Zig Ziglar

I'm "It"

The three most-important-to-me things I will do tomorrow:

TODAY'S DATE:

T

Thanks-Giving

A

Act-Knowledge-ments

G

Gifts

I'm "It"

The three most-important-to-me things I will do tomorrow:

Either you look at the universe as a very poor creation out of which no one can make anything or you look at your own life and your own part in the universe as infinitely rich, . . . opening out into infinite further possibilities . . .

~ Thomas Merton

TODAY'S DATE:

T
Thanks-Giving

A
Act-Knowledge-ments

G
Gifts

To affect the quality of the day, that is the highest of arts. Every man is tasked to make his life, even in its details, worthy of the contemplation of his most elevated and critical hour.

~ Henry David Thoreau

I'm "It"
The three most-important-to-me things I will do tomorrow:

TODAY'S DATE:

T
Thanks-Giving

A
Act-Knowledge-ments

G
Gifts

The real gift of gratitude is that the more grateful you are, the more present you become.

~ Robert Holden

I'm "It"

The three most-important-to-me things I will do tomorrow:

TODAY'S DATE:

T
Thanks-Giving

A
Act-Knowledge-ments

G
Gifts

We are shaped by those who have loved us and by those who have refused to love us.

~ Father John Powell, S. J.

I'm "It"

The three most-important-to-me things I will do tomorrow:

TODAY'S DATE:

T
Thanks-Giving

A
Act-Knowledge-ments

G
Gifts

Always bear in mind that your own resolution to succeed is more important than any other.

~ Abraham Lincoln

I'm "It"

The three most-important-to-me things I will do tomorrow:

TODAY'S DATE:

T
Thanks-Giving

A
Act-Knowledge-ments

G
Gifts

The scariest moment is always just before you start.

~ Stephen King

I'm "It"
The three most-important-to-me things I will do tomorrow:

TODAY'S DATE:

T

Thanks-Giving

A

Act-Knowledge-ments

G

Gifts

I just don't see that being a pessimist helps us in any way in life. And I have full faith in the power of the imagination . . .

~ Naomi Shihab Nye

I'm "It"

The three most-important-to-me things I will do tomorrow:

TODAY'S DATE:

T
Thanks-Giving

A
Act-Knowledge-ments

G
Gifts

A whole stack of memories never equal one little hope.

~ Charles M. Schulz

I'm "It"
The three most-important-to-me things I will do tomorrow:

TODAY'S DATE:

T
Thanks-Giving

A
Act-Knowledge-ments

G
Gifts

In a gentle way, you can shake the world.

~ Mahatma Gandhi

I'm "It"

The three most-important-to-me things I will do tomorrow:

T
Thanks-Giving

A
Act-Knowledge-ments

G
Gifts

Kindness in words creates confidence. Kindness in thinking creates profoundness. Kindness in giving creates love.

~ Lao Tzu

I'm "It"

The three most-important-to-me things I will do tomorrow:

TODAY'S DATE:

T
Thanks-Giving

A
Act-Knowledge-ments

G
Gifts

Things turn out best for people who make the best of the way things turn out.

~ John Wooden

I'm "It"
The three most-important-to-me things I will do tomorrow:

TODAY'S DATE:

T

Thanks-Giving

A

Act-Knowledge-ments

G

Gifts

*One can never pay in gratitude;
one can only pay 'in kind'
somewhere else in life.*

~ Anne Morrow Lindbergh

I'm "It"

The three most-important-to-me things I will do tomorrow:

TODAY'S DATE:

T
Thanks-Giving

A
Act-Knowledge-ments

G
Gifts

But what we call our despair is often only the painful eagerness of unfed hope.

~ George Eliot

I'm "It"

The three most-important-to-me things I will do tomorrow:

TODAY'S DATE:

T
Thanks-Giving

A
Act-Knowledge-ments

G
Gifts

...we cannot even determine after a while what's good, what's bad. What we thought a blessing has such thorns, we can hardly hold it in our hands, while what we thought was terrible turns out to wear a crown.

~ Sophy Burnham

I'm "It"

The three most-important-to-me things I will do tomorrow:

TODAY'S DATE:

T

Thanks-Giving

A

Act-Knowledge-ments

G

Gifts

It is impossible to feel grateful and depressed in the same moment.

~ Naomi Williams

I'm "It"

The three most-important-to-me things I will do tomorrow:

T

Thanks-Giving

A

Act-Knowledge-ments

G

Gifts

When I started counting my blessings, my whole life turned around.

~ Willie Nelson

I'm "It"

The three most-important-to-me things I will do tomorrow:

TODAY'S DATE:

T	A	G
Thanks-Giving	Act-Knowledge-ments	Gifts

Life can only be understood backwards; but it must be lived forwards.

~ Søren Kierkegaard

I'm "It"

The three most-important-to-me things I will do tomorrow:

T

Thanks-Giving

A

Act-Knowledge-ments

G

Gifts

There is only one happiness in this life, to love and be loved.

~ George Sand

I'm "It"

The three most-important-to-me things I will do tomorrow:

TODAY'S DATE:

T
Thanks-Giving

A
Act-Knowledge-ments

G
Gifts

Find the good and praise it.

~ Alex Haley

I'm "It"

The three most-important-to-me things I will do tomorrow:

TODAY'S DATE:

T
Thanks-Giving

A
Act-Knowledge-ments

G
Gifts

Develop interest in life as you see it; in people, things, literature, music—the world is so rich, simply throbbing with rich treasures, beautiful souls and interesting people. Forget yourself.

~ Henry Miller

I'm "It"

The three most-important-to-me things I will do tomorrow:

TODAY'S DATE:

T	**A**	**G**
Thanks-Giving	Act-Knowledge-ments	Gifts

It's kind of fun to do the impossible.

~ Walt Disney

I'm "It"

The three most-important-to-me things I will do tomorrow:

TODAY'S DATE:

T
Thanks-Giving

A
Act-Knowledge-ments

G
Gifts

And now go, and make interesting mistakes, make amazing mistakes, make glorious and fantastic mistakes. Break rules. Leave the world more interesting for your being here. Make good art.

~ Neil Gaiman

I'm "It"

The three most-important-to-me things I will do tomorrow:

TODAY'S DATE:

T
Thanks-Giving

A
Act-Knowledge-ments

G
Gifts

To live a life of gratitude is to open our eyes to the countless ways we are supported by the world around us.

~ Gregg Krech

I'm "It"

The three most-important-to-me things I will do tomorrow:

TODAY'S DATE:

T
Thanks-Giving

A
Act-Knowledge-ments

G
Gifts

No matter what sort of difficulties, how painful experience is, if we lose our hope, that's our real disaster.

~ the 14th Dalai Lama

I'm "It"

The three most-important-to-me things I will do tomorrow:

TODAY'S DATE:

T

Thanks-Giving

A

Act-Knowledge-ments

G

Gifts

May we walk in faith all the days of our life—confident in your Divine Presence, even in times of trouble, and with assurance for what is and all that is to be.

~ Nan Merrill in *Psalms for Praying*, excerpt from Psalm 106

I'm "It"

The three most-important-to-me things I will do tomorrow:

TODAY'S DATE:

T
Thanks-Giving

A
Act-Knowledge-ments

G
Gifts

Although the world is full of suffering, it is also full of the overcoming of it.

~ Helen Keller

I'm "It"

The three most-important-to-me things I will do tomorrow:

TODAY'S DATE:

T
Thanks-Giving

A
Act-Knowledge-ments

G
Gifts

An adventure is only an inconvenience rightly considered. An inconvenience is an adventure wrongly considered.

~ .G.K. Chesterton

I'm "It"

The three most-important-to-me things I will do tomorrow:

TODAY'S DATE:

T
Thanks-Giving

A
Act-Knowledge-ments

G
Gifts

Some things have to be believed o be seen.

~ Ralph Hodgson

I'm "It"
The three most-important-to-me things I will do tomorrow:

TODAY'S DATE:

T
Thanks-Giving

A
Act-Knowledge-ments

G
Gifts

Beware the barrenness of a busy life.

~ Socrates

I'm "It"

The three most-important-to-me things I will do tomorrow:

TODAY'S DATE:

T
Thanks-Giving

A
Act-Knowledge-ments

G
Gifts

What lies behind us and what lies before us are tiny matters compared to what lies within us.

~ Henry Stanley Haskins

I'm "It"

The three most-important-to-me things I will do tomorrow:

TODAY'S DATE:

T
Thanks-Giving

A
Act-Knowledge-ments

G
Gifts

Listening to your own heart, you will start moving in the right direction, without ever thinking of what is right and what is wrong.

~ Osho

I'm "It"
The three most-important-to-me things I will do tomorrow:

TODAY'S DATE:

T
Thanks-Giving

A
Act-Knowledge-ments

G
Gifts

Nothing great was ever achieved without enthusiasm.

~ Ralph Waldo Emerson

I'm "It"
The three most-important-to-me things I will do tomorrow:

TODAY'S DATE:

T
Thanks-Giving

A
Act-Knowledge-ments

G
Gifts

Chance favors those in motion.

~ Laurence Shames

I'm "It"
The three most-important-to-me things I will do tomorrow:

TODAY'S DATE:

T
Thanks-Giving

A
Act-Knowledge-ments

G
Gifts

*Everyone needs his memories.
They keep the wolf of
insignificance from the door.*

~ Saul Bellow

I'm "It"

The three most-important-to-me things I will do tomorrow:

TODAY'S DATE:

T
Thanks-Giving

A
Act-Knowledge-ments

G
Gifts

One way to say yes is to say no to everything that does not nourish and entice our secret inner life out into the world.

~ David Whyte

I'm "It"

The three most-important-to-me things I will do tomorrow:

TODAY'S DATE:

T
Thanks-Giving

A
Act-Knowledge-ments

G
Gifts

Study nature, love nature, stay close to nature. It will never fail you.

~ Frank Lloyd Wright

I'm "It"

The three most-important-to-me things I will do tomorrow:

TODAY'S DATE:

T
Thanks-Giving

A
Act-Knowledge-ments

G
Gifts

Once we believe in ourselves, we can risk curiosity, wonder, spontaneous delight, or any experience that reveals the human spirit.

~ e.e. cummings

I'm "It"

The three most-important-to-me things I will do tomorrow:

TODAY'S DATE:

T
Thanks-Giving

A
Act-Knowledge-ments

G
Gifts

And then there is the most dangerous risk of all—the risk of spending your life not doing what you want on the bet you can buy yourself the freedom to do it later.

~ Randy Komisar

I'm "It"

The three most-important-to-me things I will do tomorrow:

TODAY'S DATE:

T
Thanks-Giving

A
Act-Knowledge-ments

G
Gifts

What can we make of the inexpressible joy of children? It is a kind of gratitude, I think—the gratitude of the ten-year-old who wakes to her own energy and the brisk challenge of the world.

~ Annie Dillard

I'm "It"

The three most-important-to-me things I will do tomorrow:

TODAY'S DATE:

T
Thanks-Giving

A
Act-Knowledge-ments

G
Gifts

The secret of getting ahead is getting started.

~ Mark Twain

I'm "It"

The three most-important-to-me things I will do tomorrow:

TODAY'S DATE:

T
Thanks-Giving

A
Act-Knowledge-ments

G
Gifts

Life is no "brief candle" for me. It is a sort of splendid torch which I have got hold of for the moment, and I want to make it burn as brightly as possible before handing it on to future generations.

~ George Bernard Shaw

I'm "It"
The three most-important-to-me things I will do tomorrow:

TODAY'S DATE:

T
Thanks-Giving

A
Act-Knowledge-ments

G
Gifts

And above all, watch with glittering eyes the whole world around you because the greatest secrets are always hidden in the most unlikely places. Those who don't believe in magic will never find it.

~ Roald Dahl

I'm "It"

The three most-important-to-me things I will do tomorrow:

TODAY'S DATE:

T
Thanks-Giving

A
Act-Knowledge-ments

G
Gifts

Shoot for the moon and if you miss you will still be among the stars.

~ Les Brown

I'm "It"

The three most-important-to-me things I will do tomorrow:

TODAY'S DATE:

T

Thanks-Giving

A

Act-Knowledge-ments

G

Gifts

Never let the odds keep you from doing what you know in your heart you were meant to do.

~ H. Jackson Brown Jr.

I'm "It"

The three most-important-to-me things I will do tomorrow:

TODAY'S DATE:

T
Thanks-Giving

A
Act-Knowledge-ments

G
Gifts

Always do your best. What you plant now, you will harvest later.

~ Og Mandino

I'm "It"
The three most-important-to-me things I will do tomorrow:

TODAY'S DATE:

T
Thanks-Giving

A
Act-Knowledge-ments

G
Gifts

Everything can be taken from a man but one thing: the last of human freedoms - to choose one's attitude in any given set of circumstances, to choose one's own way.

~ Viktor E. Frankl

I'm "It"

The three most-important-to-me things I will do tomorrow:

TODAY'S DATE:

T
Thanks-Giving

A
Act-Knowledge-ments

G
Gifts

The greatest healing therapy is friendship and love.

~ Hubert H. Humphrey

I'm "It"

The three most-important-to-me things I will do tomorrow:

TODAY'S DATE:

T
Thanks-Giving

A
Act-Knowledge-ments

G
Gifts

Don't let what you cannot do interfere with what you can do.

~ John Wooden

I'm "It"

The three most-important-to-me things I will do tomorrow:

TODAY'S DATE:

T
Thanks-Giving

A
Act-Knowledge-ments

G
Gifts

It feels good to be lost in the right direction.

~ Unknown

I'm "It"

The three most-important-to-me things I will do tomorrow:

T
Thanks-Giving

A
Act-Knowledge-ments

G
Gifts

Faith, Waiting in the heart of a seed, Promises a miracle of life which cannot prove at once.

~ Kabir

I'm "It"

The three most-important-to-me things I will do tomorrow:

TODAY'S DATE:

T
Thanks-Giving

A
Act-Knowledge-ments

G
Gifts

Peace is the beauty of life. It is sunshine. It is the smile of a child, the love of a mother, the joy of a father, the togetherness of a family. It is the advancement of man, the victory of a just cause, the triumph of truth.

~ Menachem Begin

I'm "It"

The three most-important-to-me things I will do tomorrow:

TODAY'S DATE:

T
Thanks-Giving

A
Act-Knowledge-ments

G
Gifts

Love yourself. It is important to stay positive because beauty comes from the inside out.

~ Jenn Proske

I'm "It"
The three most-important-to-me things I will do tomorrow:

TODAY'S DATE:

T

Thanks-Giving

A

Act-Knowledge-ments

G

Gifts

Watch your thoughts, for they become words. Watch your words, for they become your actions. Watch your actions, for they become habits. Watch Watch your habits, for they become your character. And watch your character, for it becomes your destiny.

~ Margaret Thatcher

I'm "It"

The three most-important-to-me things I will do tomorrow:

TODAY'S DATE:

T
Thanks-Giving

A
Act-Knowledge-ments

G
Gifts

Begin now to be what you will be hereafter.

~ Saint Jerome

I'm "It"

The three most-important-to-me things I will do tomorrow:

TODAY'S DATE:

T

Thanks-Giving

A

Act-Knowledge-ments

G

Gifts

The brain is wider than the sky.

~ Emily Dickinson

I'm "It"

The three most-important-to-me things I will do tomorrow:

TODAY'S DATE:

T
Thanks-Giving

A
Act-Knowledge-ments

G
Gifts

When you follow your bliss doors will open where you would not have thought there would be doors, and where there wouldn't be a door for anyone else.

~ Joseph Campbell

I'm "It"

The three most-important-to-me things I will do tomorrow:

TODAY'S DATE:

T
Thanks-Giving

A
Act-Knowledge-ments

G
Gifts

You have as much laughter as you have faith.

~ Martin Luther

I'm "It"
The three most-important-to-me things I will do tomorrow:

TODAY'S DATE:

T
Thanks-Giving

A
Act-Knowledge-ments

G
Gifts

If you don't know where you are going, you will probably end up somewhere else.

~ Laurence J. Peter

I'm "It"

The three most-important-to-me things I will do tomorrow:

TODAY'S DATE:

T

Thanks-Giving

A

Act-Knowledge-ments

G

Gifts

The only way to do great work is to love what you do. If you haven't found it yet, keep looking. Don't settle. As with all matters of the heart, you'll know when you find it.

~ Steve Jobs

I'm "It"

The three most-important-to-me things I will do tomorrow:

TODAY'S DATE:

T
Thanks-Giving

A
Act-Knowledge-ments

G
Gifts

Ever tried. Ever failed. No matter. Try again. Fail again. Fail better.

~ Samuel Beckett

I'm "It"

The three most-important-to-me things I will do tomorrow:

TODAY'S DATE:

T
Thanks-Giving

A
Act-Knowledge-ments

G
Gifts

To pay attention, this is our endless and proper work.

~ Mary Oliver in "Yes! No!"

I'm "It"

The three most-important-to-me things I will do tomorrow:

TODAY'S DATE:

T
Thanks-Giving

A
Act-Knowledge-ments

G
Gifts

There is no right path. Only the one that let's you sleep soundly and wake up excited.

~ Jennifer Louden

I'm "It"

The three most-important-to-me things I will do tomorrow:

TODAY'S DATE:

T
Thanks-Giving

A
Act-Knowledge-ments

G
Gifts

It is good to have an end to journey toward, but it is the journey that matters, in the end.

~ Ernest Hemingway

I'm "It"

The three most-important-to-me things I will do tomorrow:

TODAY'S DATE:

T
Thanks-Giving

A
Act-Knowledge-ments

G
Gifts

Wherever you are, be all there.

~ Jim Elliot

I'm "It"
The three most-important-to-me things I will do tomorrow:

TODAY'S DATE:

T
Thanks-Giving

A
Act-Knowledge-ments

G
Gifts

If you don't like something, change it. If you can't change it, change your attitude.

~ Maya Angelou

I'm "It"

The three most-important-to-me things I will do tomorrow:

TODAY'S DATE:

T
Thanks-Giving

A
Act-Knowledge-ments

G
Gifts

If you have built castles in the air, your work need not be lost; that is where they should be. Now put the foundations under them.

~ Henry David Thoreau

I'm "It"
The three most-important-to-me things I will do tomorrow:

TODAY'S DATE:

T
Thanks-Giving

A
Act-Knowledge-ments

G
Gifts

Life is not always a matter of holding good cards, but sometimes, playing a poor hand well.

~ Jack London

I'm "It"

The three most-important-to-me things I will do tomorrow:

TODAY'S DATE:

T
Thanks-Giving

A
Act-Knowledge-ments

G
Gifts

With the new day comes new strength and new thoughts.

~ Eleanor Roosevelt

I'm "It"
The three most-important-to-me things I will do tomorrow:

TODAY'S DATE:

T
Thanks-Giving

A
Act-Knowledge-ments

G
Gifts

Do not ask yourself what the world needs. Ask yourself what makes you come alive, and then go do that. Because what the world needs is people who have come alive.

~ Howard Thurman

I'm "It"

The three most-important-to-me things I will do tomorrow:

TODAY'S DATE:

T
Thanks-Giving

A
Act-Knowledge-ments

G
Gifts

*Maybe I am slightly inhuman . . .
All I ever wanted to do was to
paint sunlight on the side of
a house.*

~ Edward Hopper

I'm "It"

The three most-important-to-me things I will do tomorrow:

TODAY'S DATE:

T
Thanks-Giving

A
Act-Knowledge-ments

G
Gifts

I am not the same having seen the moon shine in the other side of the world.

~ Mary Ann Radmacher

I'm "It"
The three most-important-to-me things I will do tomorrow:

TODAY'S DATE:

T
Thanks-Giving

A
Act-Knowledge-ments

G
Gifts

Our deepest fear is not that we are inadequate. Our deepest fear is that we are powerful beyond measure.

~ Marianne Williamson

I'm "It"

The three most-important-to-me things I will do tomorrow:

TODAY'S DATE:

T
Thanks-Giving

A
Act-Knowledge-ments

G
Gifts

Man cannot discover new oceans unless he has the courage to lose sight of the shore.

~ André Gide

I'm "It"
The three most-important-to-me things I will do tomorrow:

TODAY'S DATE:

T
Thanks-Giving

A
Act-Knowledge-ments

G
Gifts

Every adventure is worthwhile.

~ Amelia Earhart

I'm "It"

The three most-important-to-me things I will do tomorrow:

TODAY'S DATE:

T
Thanks-Giving

A
Act-Knowledge-ments

G
Gifts

You cannot solve a problem from the same consciousness that created it. You must learn to see the world anew.

~ Albert Einstein

I'm "It"

The three most-important-to-me things I will do tomorrow:

TODAY'S DATE:

T
Thanks-Giving

A
Act-Knowledge-ments

G
Gifts

I read and walked for miles at night along the beach, writing bad blank verse and searching endlessly for someone wonderful who would step out of the darkness and change my life. It never crossed my mind that that person could be me.

~ Anna Quindlen

I'm "It"

The three most-important-to-me things I will do tomorrow:

TODAY'S DATE:

T
Thanks-Giving

A
Act-Knowledge-ments

G
Gifts

Wherever you are, and whatever you do, be in love.

~ Rumi

I'm "It"

The three most-important-to-me things I will do tomorrow:

TODAY'S DATE:

T

Thanks-Giving

A

Act-Knowledge-ments

G

Gifts

Believe in your creativity—you will become what you consistently think of yourself.

~ John Kehoe

I'm "It"

The three most-important-to-me things I will do tomorrow:

T

Thanks-Giving

A

Act-Knowledge-ments

G

Gifts

Life isn't about finding yourself.
Life is about creating yourself.

~ George Bernard Shaw

I'm "It"

The three most-important-to-me things I will do tomorrow:

TODAY'S DATE:

T

Thanks-Giving

A

Act-Knowledge-ments

G

Gifts

Great things never came from comfort zones.

~ Neil Strauss

I'm "It"

The three most-important-to-me things I will do tomorrow:

TODAY'S DATE:

T
Thanks-Giving

A
Act-Knowledge-ments

G
Gifts

Wherever you go, go with all our heart.

~ Confucius

I'm "It"

The three most-important-to-me things I will do tomorrow:

TODAY'S DATE:

T

Thanks-Giving

A

Act-Knowledge-ments

G

Gifts

Joy is not in things; it is in us.

~ Richard Wagner

I'm "It"

The three most-important-to-me things I will do tomorrow:

TODAY'S DATE:

T

Thanks-Giving

A

Act-Knowledge-ments

G

Gifts

Mix a little foolishness with your serious plans. It is lovely to be silly at the right moment.

~ Horace

I'm "It"

The three most-important-to-me things I will do tomorrow:

TODAY'S DATE:

T

Thanks-Giving

A

Act-Knowledge-ments

G

Gifts

Whatever you can do or dream you can, begin it. Boldness has genius, power, and magic in it.

~ Johann Wolfgang Von Goethe

I'm "It"

The three most-important-to-me things I will do tomorrow:

TODAY'S DATE:

T
Thanks-Giving

A
Act-Knowledge-ments

G
Gifts

Wherever you go, no matter what the weather, always bring your own sunshine.

~ Anthony J. D'Angelo

I'm "It"

The three most-important-to-me things I will do tomorrow:

TODAY'S DATE:

T
Thanks-Giving

A
Act-Knowledge-ments

G
Gifts

Problems are not stop signs, they are guidelines.

~ Robert Schuller

I'm "It"
The three most-important-to-me things I will do tomorrow:

TODAY'S DATE:

T

Thanks-Giving

A

Act-Knowledge-ments

G

Gifts

Live as if your prayers are to be answered.

~ Unknown

I'm "It"

The three most-important-to-me things I will do tomorrow:

TODAY'S DATE:

T
Thanks-Giving

A
Act-Knowledge-ments

G
Gifts

Once you choose hope, anything's possible.

Christopher Reeve

I'm "It"

The three most-important-to-me things I will do tomorrow:

TODAY'S DATE:

T
Thanks-Giving

A
Act-Knowledge-ments

G
Gifts

Little minds are tamed and subdued by misfortune; but great minds rise above them.

~ Washington Irving

I'm "It"
The three most-important-to-me things I will do tomorrow:

TODAY'S DATE:

T
Thanks-Giving

A
Act-Knowledge-ments

G
Gifts

Most of the important things in the world have been accomplished by people who have kept on trying when there seemed to be no hope at all.

~ Dale Carnegie

I'm "It"

The three most-important-to-me things I will do tomorrow:

T

Thanks-Giving

A

Act-Knowledge-ments

G

Gifts

Faith is to believe what you do not see; the reward of this faith is to see what you believe.

~ St. Augustine

I'm "It"

The three most-important-to-me things I will do tomorrow:

TODAY'S DATE:

T

Thanks-Giving

A

Act-Knowledge-ments

G

Gifts

A problem is a chance for you to do your best.

~ Duke Ellington

I'm "It"

The three most-important-to-me things I will do tomorrow:

TODAY'S DATE:

T
Thanks-Giving

A
Act-Knowledge-ments

G
Gifts

Do not be daunted by the enormity of the world's grief. Do justly, now. Love mercy, now. Walk humbly, now. You are not obligated to complete the work, but neither are you free to abandon it.

~ Talmud

I'm "It"

The three most-important-to-me things I will do tomorrow:

TODAY'S DATE:

T
Thanks-Giving

A
Act-Knowledge-ments

G
Gifts

You cannot do a kindness too soon because you never know how soon it will be too late.

~ Ralph Waldo Emerson

I'm "It"
The three most-important-to-me things I will do tomorrow:

TODAY'S DATE:

T
Thanks-Giving

A
Act-Knowledge-ments

G
Gifts

We are all in the gutter, but some of us are looking at the stars.

~ Oscar Wilde

I'm "It"
The three most-important-to-me things I will do tomorrow:

TODAY'S DATE:

T
Thanks-Giving

A
Act-Knowledge-ments

G
Gifts

In the end, everything will be okay.
If it's not okay, it's not yet the end.

~ Fernando Sabino

I'm "It"

The three most-important-to-me things I will do tomorrow:

TODAY'S DATE:

T
Thanks-Giving

A
Act-Knowledge-ments

G
Gifts

Think big thoughts but relish small pleasures.

~ H. Jackson Brown

I'm "It"

The three most-important-to-me things I will do tomorrow:

TODAY'S DATE:

T
Thanks-Giving

A
Act-Knowledge-ments

G
Gifts

Gratitude takes nothing for granted, is never unresponsive, is constantly awakening to new wonder and to praise of the goodness of God.

~ Thomas Merton

I'm "It"

The three most-important-to-me things I will do tomorrow:

TODAY'S DATE:

T
Thanks-Giving

A
Act-Knowledge-ments

G
Gifts

I cannot endure to waste anything so precious as autumnal sunshine by staying in the house.

~ Nathaniel Hawthorne

I'm "It"
The three most-important-to-me things I will do tomorrow:

TODAY'S DATE:

T
Thanks-Giving

A
Act-Knowledge-ments

G
Gifts

Change your thoughts and you change your world.

~ Norman Vincent Peale

I'm "It"

The three most-important-to-me things I will do tomorrow:

TODAY'S DATE:

T
Thanks-Giving

A
Act-Knowledge-ments

G
Gifts

We know what we are, but know not what we may be.

~ William Shakespeare

I'm "It"

The three most-important-to-me things I will do tomorrow:

TODAY'S DATE:

T
Thanks-Giving

A
Act-Knowledge-ments

G
Gifts

There is no greater agony than bearing an untold story inside you.

~ Maya Angelou

I'm "It"

The three most-important-to-me things I will do tomorrow:

TODAY'S DATE:

T
Thanks-Giving

A
Act-Knowledge-ments

G
Gifts

*Dwell on the beauty of life. Watch
the stars, and see yourself running
with them.*

~ Marcus Aurelius

I'm "It"

The three most-important-to-me things I will do tomorrow:

TODAY'S DATE:

T

Thanks-Giving

A

Act-Knowledge-ments

G

Gifts

I'm so glad I live in a world where there are Octobers.

~ L.M. Montgomery, author of Anne of Green Gables

I'm "It"

The three most-important-to-me things I will do tomorrow:

T

Thanks-Giving

A

Act-Knowledge-ments

G

Gifts

Embrace the glorious mess that you are.

~ Elizabeth Gilbert

I'm "It"

The three most-important-to-me things I will do tomorrow:

TODAY'S DATE:

T
Thanks-Giving

A
Act-Knowledge-ments

G
Gifts

The best way to predict the future is to create it.

~ Abraham Lincoln

I'm "It"

The three most-important-to-me things I will do tomorrow:

TODAY'S DATE:

T
Thanks-Giving

A
Act-Knowledge-ments

G
Gifts

The first step is you have to say that you can.

~ Will Smith

I'm "It"

The three most-important-to-me things I will do tomorrow:

TODAY'S DATE:

T
Thanks-Giving

A
Act-Knowledge-ments

G
Gifts

You must do the thing you think you cannot do.

~ Eleanor Roosevelt

I'm "It"

The three most-important-to-me things I will do tomorrow:

TODAY'S DATE:

T
Thanks-Giving

A
Act-Knowledge-ments

G
Gifts

*That's what a minute
said to an hour
Without me
you are nothing*

*~ Naomi Shihab Nye in
"To Manage"*

I'm "It"

The three most-important-to-me things I will do tomorrow:

TODAY'S DATE:

T
Thanks-Giving

A
Act-Knowledge-ments

G
Gifts

Unexpected wonders happen, not on schedule or when you expect or want them to happen, but if you keep hanging around, they do happen.

~ Wendell Berry

I'm "It"
The three most-important-to-me things I will do tomorrow:

TODAY'S DATE:

T
Thanks-Giving

A
Act-Knowledge-ments

G
Gifts

Optimism is the faith that leads to achievement. Nothing can be done without hope or confidence.

~ Helen Keller

I'm "It"

The three most-important-to-me things I will do tomorrow:

TODAY'S DATE:

T
Thanks-Giving

A
Act-Knowledge-ments

G
Gifts

We don't laugh because we're happy—we're happy because we laugh.

William James

I'm "It"

The three most-important-to-me things I will do tomorrow:

TODAY'S DATE:

T
Thanks-Giving

A
Act-Knowledge-ments

G
Gifts

Our greatest weakness lies in giving up. The most certain way to succeed is always to try just one more time.

~ Thomas Edison

I'm "It"

The three most-important-to-me things I will do tomorrow:

TODAY'S DATE:

T
Thanks-Giving

A
Act-Knowledge-ments

G
Gifts

To have striven, to have made an effort, to have been true to certain ideals—this alone is worth the struggle.

~ Sir William Osler

I'm "It"

The three most-important-to-me things I will do tomorrow:

TODAY'S DATE:

T
Thanks-Giving

A
Act-Knowledge-ments

G
Gifts

I am grateful for what I am and what I have. My thanksgiving is perpetual.

~ Henry David Thoreau

I'm "It"

The three most-important-to-me things I will do tomorrow:

TODAY'S DATE:

T
Thanks-Giving

A
Act-Knowledge-ments

G
Gifts

You cannot protect yourself from sadness without protecting yourself from happiness.

~ Jonathan Safran Foer

I'm "It"

The three most-important-to-me things I will do tomorrow:

TODAY'S DATE:

T
Thanks-Giving

A
Act-Knowledge-ments

G
Gifts

The most basic and powerful way to connect to another person is to listen. Just listen. Perhaps the most important thing we ever give each other is our attention.... A loving silence often has far more power to heal and to connect than the most well-intentioned words.

~ Rachel Naomi Remen

I'm "It"

The three most-important-to-me things I will do tomorrow:

TODAY'S DATE:

T
Thanks-Giving

A
Act-Knowledge-ments

G
Gifts

Each morning we are born again. What we do today is what matters most.

~ Buddha

I'm "It"

The three most-important-to-me things I will do tomorrow:

TODAY'S DATE:

T

Thanks-Giving

A

Act-Knowledge-ments

G

Gifts

If opportunity doesn't knock, build a door.

~ Milton Berle

I'm "It"

The three most-important-to-me things I will do tomorrow:

TODAY'S DATE:

T
Thanks-Giving

A
Act-Knowledge-ments

G
Gifts

Whatever you are, try to be a good one.

~ William Makepeace Thackeray

I'm "It"

The three most-important-to-me things I will do tomorrow:

TODAY'S DATE:

T	A	G
Thanks-Giving	Act-Knowledge-ments	Gifts

The future starts today, not tomorrow.

~ Pope John Paul II

I'm "It"

The three most-important-to-me things I will do tomorrow:

TODAY'S DATE:

T
Thanks-Giving

A
Act-Knowledge-ments

G
Gifts

If you do not change direction, you may end up where you are heading.

~ Lao Tzu

I'm "It"

The three most-important-to-me things I will do tomorrow:

T
Thanks-Giving

A
Act-Knowledge-ments

G
Gifts

The supreme accomplishment is to blur the line between work and play.

~ Arnold Toynbee

I'm "It"

The three most-important-to-me things I will do tomorrow:

TODAY'S DATE:

T
Thanks-Giving

A
Act-Knowledge-ments

G
Gifts

Beyond a wholesome discipline,
be gentle with yourself.

~ Max Ehrmann
in "Desiderata"

I'm "It"

The three most-important-to-me things I will do tomorrow:

TODAY'S DATE:

T
Thanks-Giving

A
Act-Knowledge-ments

G
Gifts

We are meant to midwife dreams for one another.

~ Julia Cameron

I'm "It"
The three most-important-to-me things I will do tomorrow:

TODAY'S DATE:

T
Thanks-Giving

A
Act-Knowledge-ments

G
Gifts

Nothing would be done at all if a man waited until he could do it so well that no one could find fault with it.

~ Cardinal Newman

I'm "It"

The three most-important-to-me things I will do tomorrow:

TODAY'S DATE:	

T	**A**	**G**
Thanks-Giving	Act-Knowledge-ments	Gifts

One's destination is never a place,
but a new way of seeing things.

~ Henry Miller

I'm "It"

The three most-important-to-me things I will do tomorrow:

TODAY'S DATE:

T
Thanks-Giving

A
Act-Knowledge-ments

G
Gifts

Cry. Forgive. Learn. Move on. Let your tears water the seeds of your future happiness.

~ Steve Maraboli

I'm "It"

The three most-important-to-me things I will do tomorrow:

TODAY'S DATE:

T
Thanks-Giving

A
Act-Knowledge-ments

G
Gifts

We can never be born enough . . . birth is a supremely welcome mystery, the mystery of growing: the mystery which happens only and whenever we are faithful to ourselves.

~ e.e. cummings

I'm "It"
The three most-important-to-me things I will do tomorrow:

TODAY'S DATE:

T
Thanks-Giving

A
Act-Knowledge-ments

G
Gifts

They say a person needs just three things to be truly happy in this world: someone to love, something to do, and something to hope for.

~ Tom Bodett

I'm "It"
The three most-important-to-me things I will do tomorrow:

TODAY'S DATE:

T
Thanks-Giving

A
Act-Knowledge-ments

G
Gifts

Man needs difficulties; they are necessary for health.

~ Carl Jung

I'm "It"

The three most-important-to-me things I will do tomorrow:

TODAY'S DATE:

T
Thanks-Giving

A
Act-Knowledge-ments

G
Gifts

Always be a little kinder than necessary.

~ Sir James M. Barrie

I'm "It"

The three most-important-to-me things I will do tomorrow:

TODAY'S DATE:

T
Thanks-Giving

A
Act-Knowledge-ments

G
Gifts

The best is yet to be.

~ Robert Browning

I'm "It"
The three most-important-to-me things I will do tomorrow:

TODAY'S DATE:

T
Thanks-Giving

A
Act-Knowledge-ments

G
Gifts

If you can dream it, then you can achieve it. You will get all you want in life if you help enough other people get what they want.

~ Zig Ziglar

I'm "It"

The three most-important-to-me things I will do tomorrow:

TODAY'S DATE:

T
Thanks-Giving

A
Act-Knowledge-ments

G
Gifts

Gratitude turns what we have into enough.

~ Aesop

I'm "It"

The three most-important-to-me things I will do tomorrow:

TODAY'S DATE:

T
Thanks-Giving

A
Act-Knowledge-ments

G
Gifts

What good is the warmth of summer, without the cold of winter to give it sweetness?

~ John Steinbeck

I'm "It"
The three most-important-to-me things I will do tomorrow:

TODAY'S DATE:

T
Thanks-Giving

A
Act-Knowledge-ments

G
Gifts

Darkness cannot drive out darkness; only light can do that. Hate cannot drive out hate; only love can do that.

~ Martin Luther King, Jr.

I'm "It"

The three most-important-to-me things I will do tomorrow:

T

Thanks-Giving

A

Act-Knowledge-ments

G

Gifts

We do not stop playing because we grow old, we grow old because we stop playing.

~ George Bernard Shaw

I'm "It"

The three most-important-to-me things I will do tomorrow:

TODAY'S DATE:

T
Thanks-Giving

A
Act-Knowledge-ments

G
Gifts

Even this later it happens:
the coming of love, the coming
of light. . . .

~ Mark Strand in
"The Coming of Light"

I'm "It"

The three most-important-to-me things I will do tomorrow:

TODAY'S DATE:

T
Thanks-Giving

A
Act-Knowledge-ments

G
Gifts

What's a heart for?

~ Annie Dillard

I'm "It"
The three most-important-to-me things I will do tomorrow:

TODAY'S DATE:

T
Thanks-Giving

A
Act-Knowledge-ments

G
Gifts

There is nothing for you to go back and live over, or fix, or feel regret about now. Every part of your life has unfolded just right. . . . Go forth in joy, and get on with it.

~ Abraham-Hicks

I'm "It"

The three most-important-to-me things I will do tomorrow:

TODAY'S DATE:

T
Thanks-Giving

A
Act-Knowledge-ments

G
Gifts

Happiness is not a state to arrive at, but a manner of traveling.

~ Margaret Lee Runbeck

I'm "It"
The three most-important-to-me things I will do tomorrow:

TODAY'S DATE:

T
Thanks-Giving

A
Act-Knowledge-ments

G
Gifts

As for me, I could leave the world with today in my eyes.

~ Sook, in Truman Capote's "A Christmas Story"

I'm "It"
The three most-important-to-me things I will do tomorrow:

TODAY'S DATE:

T
Thanks-Giving

A
Act-Knowledge-ments

G
Gifts

Twenty years from now you will be more disappointed by the things you didn't do than by the ones you did. So throw off the bowlines. Sail away from the safe harbor. Catch the trade winds in your sails. Explore. Dream. Discover.

~ Mark Twain

I'm "It"

The three most-important-to-me things I will do tomorrow:

TODAY'S DATE:

T
Thanks-Giving

A
Act-Knowledge-ments

G
Gifts

What lies behind us and lies before us are small matters compared to what lies within us.

~ Ralph Waldo Emerson

I'm "It"

The three most-important-to-me things I will do tomorrow:

TODAY'S DATE:

T
Thanks-Giving

A
Act-Knowledge-ments

G
Gifts

Year's end is neither an end nor a beginning but a going on, with all the wisdom that experience can instill in us.

~ Hal Borland

I'm "It"
The three most-important-to-me things I will do tomorrow:

TODAY'S DATE:

T
Thanks-Giving

A
Act-Knowledge-ments

G
Gifts

What we call the beginning is often the end. And to make an end is to make a beginning. The end is where we start from.

~ T.S. Eliot

I'm "It"

The three most-important-to-me things I will do tomorrow:

Made in the USA
Columbia, SC
03 December 2019